Evolution and Systematics

Otto T. Solbrig

Harvard University

The Macmillan Company, New York

Collier–Macmillan Limited, London

CURRENT CONCEPTS IN BIOLOGY

A MACMILLAN SERIES

NORMAN H. GILES, WALTER KENWORTHY, JOHN G. TORREY, Editors

The Macmillan Company, New York

Collier–Macmillan Canada, Ltd., Toronto, Ontario

Printed in the United States of America

Designed by Andrew P. Zutis

*We are not here
concerned with hopes or fears,
only with the truth
as far as our reason
permits us to discover it.*

CHARLES DARWIN

Preface

THE DIVERSITY of living beings is the concern of this book. Some of the major evolutionary principles and basic facts used to ascertain relationships between organisms are analyzed, from origin of life to fossilization. The emphasis is on the phenomena occurring at the level of population, for natural selection operates in populations and populations are what really evolve. The diversity of living beings—their environments, life histories, and distributions over the surface of the earth—is often studied more or less independently from the more analytical interpretations of life in terms of function which tend to look in atoms and molecules for the ultimate causes of the behavior of living matter. This is unfortunate, inasmuch as both approaches are important and somewhat interdependent.

The principle of evolution by natural selection is the most important unifying concept in biology. It applies equally well to organisms and to molecules. Darwin's work, supplemented by the subsequent development of his ideas, has provided an explanation for the diversity of living forms. It has also provided a meaning—not a purposeful meaning, to be sure, but one in terms of selection and adaptation. A second set of unifying concepts in biology was provided by the geneticists. At times, genetics has appeared to deny evolution—at least, evolution according to Darwin. As time has gone by, however, discrepancies have been erased, and genetic principles have contributed materially to the development of the modern theory of evolution.

Today we are in the midst of a chemical revolution in biology—or, as it is called, a "molecular" revolution. Molecular biology is adding a new dimension, and has successfully closed the gap which once existed between the organic and the inorganic. The new information promises to make the study of the diversity of organisms more interesting than ever.

When faced with an unknown object, we acquire knowledge by obtaining answers to three basic questions: (1) How does it work? (2) Where did it come from—i.e. what is its history? and (3) What is its relationship to other objects? Man has been asking these questions of

45453

himself and the world that surrounds him since he became a rational being. Morphology, anatomy, physiology, and today molecular biology try to answer the first question, "How?" Evolutionary biology is concerned with the past history of organisms and also with the mechanism of change. Systematics is the science that tries to ascertain the relationships of organisms to each other using the information provided by the morphologists, anatomists, physiologists, and even the molecular biologists, as well as by the evolutionists. Although we may separate the function of an organ from its past history in order properly to study and experiment, it is becoming increasingly clear that full knowledge in biology is possible only when equal attention is paid to all aspects of an organism, from its chemistry to its geological record. Thus the systematist, probably more than any other scientist, needs to be aware of the complete nature of biology and of all aspects of the scientific knowledge bearing upon it.

The present book is intended for the beginning student. It does not require any previous knowledge of the subject. It does require, though, some acquaintance with biology—for example, some understanding of cell division and of the basic facts about plants and animals. Limitations of space dictate that much interesting material be left untouched or barely mentioned. It is hoped that the interested student will pursue these matters further; to this end, a short bibliography is provided at the end of each chapter. It should be remembered that the general principles and major ideas emphasized are valid only as far as the evidence on which they are based is valid; new facts may, and probably will, change some of our ideas. The student therefore should make an effort to become acquainted with the observational and experimental evidence on which general principles are based. Finally, it is hoped that at least some of the readers may become interested in pursuing and eventually answering some of the many evolutionary problems that still remain unanswered.

I am very grateful to the many people who have aided in the development of this book—in particular, my former teachers at the University of California and my colleagues and students at Harvard. I want to acknowledge specially the help of Professors Ernst Mayr and Reed C. Rollins in reading the manuscript in its entirety. Professor Lincoln Constance, Dr. Jean Langenheim, and Mr. Hugh Winning also read parts of the manuscript and made valuable suggestions. I am also indebted to Dr. D. S. Falconer and to Oliver & Boyd Ltd. of Edinburgh for their permission to reprint Table 2·1 and Figure 2·2 from their book *Introduction to Quantitative Genetics*. And, finally, I am very grateful for the editorial advice of my wife, Roberta.

O. T. S.

Contents

Evolution and the Principle of Natural Selection

APPROXIMATELY HALF A MILLION species of living plants and twice as many species of animals have been found and described to date, and it is estimated that there might still be one or two million more undescribed species. Furthermore it is believed that the number of species of plants and animals, now extinct, which once inhabited the earth is five to nine times the number of those living today. The realization a hundred years ago that all these species are the result of evolution through natural selection in the last three billion years was one of the most significant advances in biology. The slow recognition in our days that all living creatures consist entirely of chemicals has had an equally great impact on biology. It used to be believed that "dead" and "living" matter were of different natures, but today we know that this is not so. Since living matter is more complex, more highly organized, than nonliving matter, organisms must have evolved from simpler, nonliving components. By tracing the origin of living forms we gain important glimpses into the very nature of life.

To be sure, our understanding of the origin of life is at present far from complete. Many of our ideas are speculative. They are based on the properties of present-day organisms and on data submitted by physicists, chemists, geologists, and astronomers. At best, then, we have an idea as to how life could have arisen from nonlife, but this provides only some background and a glimpse about the nature of life.

Origin of Terrestrial Life

The origin and nature of life have interested man ever since he became a rational being. One of the earliest explanations brought forward was that life originated by spontaneous generation from nonliving matter. Undoubtedly the observation that all dead bodies decompose into simpler elements, that everything "reverts to earth," and ignorance about the life of maggots, molds, and microscopic organisms, which appeared to come from nowhere, led to this idea. When Pasteur in the late nineteenth century demonstrated that spontaneous generation does not take place on earth, spontaneous generation seemed scientifically untenable, and for a time the idea was abandoned. This type of generation is not possible today because of the presence of living organisms that feed on every organic substance available. This prevents the transformation of simple organic substances into more complex matter, a very slow process indeed.

But conditions on earth were different at one time. At the dawn of our planet's existence, no organisms were present, and the slowness of the process by which simple chemicals became transformed into more complex ones did not matter, since lack of time was not a factor. Under these conditions spontaneous generation through the slow transformation of atoms and molecules into simple chemical compounds, and of these compounds into more and more complex substances, leading eventually to living organisms, is believed to have taken place. For this to occur certain conditions were necessary, such as temperatures in the narrow range between the freezing and boiling points of water, and a source of energy, which in this case was solar radiation. Eventually water started accumulating on the earth, and oceans were formed in which the various chemical compounds dissolved. This facilitated reactions among the different chemicals and the formation of still more complex substances. Eventually compounds were formed that were capable of producing more of their own kind by a process of duplication. Duplication, or reproduction, is the basic property of life. When a substance originated that had the property of reproducing its own kind, no matter how simple that substance was, what we call life had originated. From there on, by evolution through natural selection, the simple organisms became gradually more complex, acquiring the traits and functions that are characteristic of present-day plants and animals.

The nature of all the steps leading to the formation of life is not known. Nevertheless several plausible ways have been proposed. Since we have no precise way of knowing what the exact conditions on earth were at the time, there is a great deal of conjecture involved. Also, because of the presently changed conditions of our planet and the slowness of the process, it is impossible to verify experimentally the proposed pathways that led to the origin of living matter. This notwithstanding, a simple experiment showing the soundness of the fundamental idea was performed by Stanley L. Miller of the University of Chicago. He circulated in a sealed

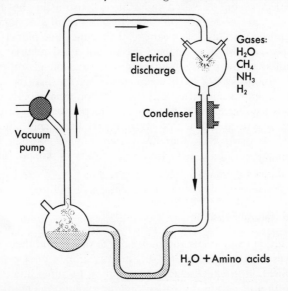

Figure 1·1. Sketch of the experiment conducted by S. L. Miller. The gases methane, ammonia, hydrogen, and water vapor were circulated for about a week. In each cycle they were subjected to an electrical discharge. Amino acids were recovered from the trap at the bottom.

circuit a mixture of the gases methane, ammonia, hydrogen, and water vapor—universally accepted as the most likely to have been present in the early atmosphere. At a certain point in the circuit an electrical discharge simulating lightning was produced (Figure 1·1). This experiment was run intermittently for a week, and when it was terminated and the products analyzed, minute quantities of amino acids—the basic components of proteins, and one of the principal chemical organic substances of any living being—had been formed. The main point this experiment proves is that under certain set conditions more complex substances can be formed from simpler compounds, a very remarkable fact indeed.

One of the more fascinating aspects of this scheme is that once the right conditions were present on the earth, the formation of complex organic substances and life was the inevitable consequence.

In turn, the position of the earth in the solar system probably made the presence of these conditions an inevitable event. But the sun is not a special type of star in the universe; the likes of it are counted by the millions in our galaxy alone, and by the billions in the totality of the cosmos. According to the Harvard astronomer Harlow Shapley, of the approximately 10^{20} stars (100,000,000,000,-000,000,000, or one hundred quintillion) existing in the universe, 20 per cent are essentially identical to our sun in size, luminosity, and chemistry. If only 1 per cent of these suns have planets, and if only 1 per cent of these planets are in positions, relative to their suns, similar to the earth's position to our sun, some form of life is probable for at least 2×10^{15} planets. If so, life may be a rather common phenomenon after all! In addition Shapley thinks that conditions leading to what we call life are possible also in crusted-over stars—that is, stars with a warm center but a cold outer crust. It should be made clear that life is here defined as some kind of self-duplicating system, not necessarily forms of life as found on earth.

The Concept of Natural Selection

The evolution from atoms and molecules to simple and then complex substances, and from these to still more complex ones capable of self-duplication, is called chemical evolution to differentiate it from the evolution of organisms, called organic evolution. The difference between these two kinds of evolution lies in the fundamental nature of living matter: the capacity to reproduce itself. In the stages leading to the formation of life, more and more complex substances in ever larger quantities were formed, as more energy was received from the sun and as more chemicals reacted with each other. These substances were capable of growing in a fashion similar to the growth of a crystal, and by accidental breakage could divide into several units. But this type of growth does not yet represent reproduction. The moment the property of self-duplication was acquired, that chemical substance—most likely a nucleic acid similar to or identical with the DNA found in chromosomes of present-day plants and animals—could form more of its own at the expense of other and probably simpler compounds. In other words it could grow and reproduce. Once two substances, or two strains of the same chemical have this same property, the one that produces the largest number of surviving "offspring" will obviously become more abundant. This is the essence of the process called natural selection, which is an exclusive characteristic of organic evolution.

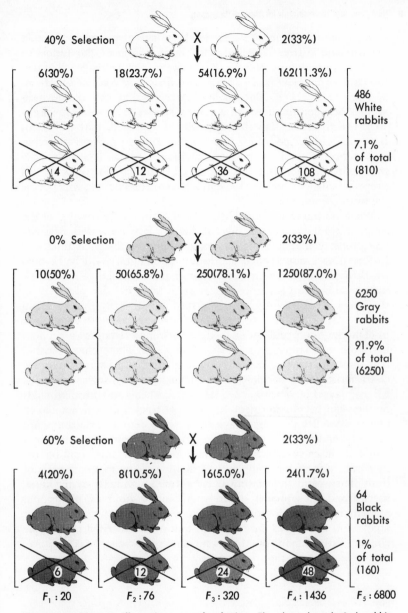

Figure 1·2. Diagram illustrating natural selection. The three hypothetical rabbit pairs differ only in color. The white and black rabbits being more conspicuous lose 40% and 60% of their progeny before they can reproduce. After five generations of this intense selection, the white rabbits account for only 7% of the total and the black for only 1%, although their numbers have increased from 2 to 486 and 64 respectively.

The concept of natural selection was first proposed by Charles Darwin and Alfred Wallace at the same session of the Linnaean Society of London on July 1, 1858. A year later Darwin elaborated his ideas in his now famous book *The Origin of Species by Means of Natural Selection.* Darwin had observed that not all the individuals of a certain kind—of a certain species to be more precise—were exactly alike. Any characteristic, he reasoned, that will result in the individuals possessing it producing a larger progeny surviving to adulthood than individuals not having this trait will become more prevalent. As time goes by, the number of individuals with this property will increase until eventually most individuals will possess the trait (Figure 1·2).

What are the characters that result in an increased survival of the progeny? Many and exceedingly varied, as Darwin realized. Basically any property that increases the adaptability of the individual and his breeding group (called a breeding population) will be favored by natural selection. Any inherited characteristic that makes the individual or the population possessing it more capable of surviving the rigors of the environment is termed adaptive. By this we mean characteristics that will result in circumventing adverse conditions, in obtaining more and better food, in avoiding predators, in producing more and larger progenies, and so forth. These characteristics will result in survival of a larger number of the young. Adaptive characteristics can be morphological, such as the presence of thick fur and layers of subcutaneous fat in polar bears to withstand cold; or they can be physiological, as in apple trees that will not bloom and fruit well unless they have been exposed to a certain amount of cold—an adaptation that insures the plant against blooming in a late fall or early winter "Indian summer"; or they can be behavioral, such as the complex and highly specific mating rituals of birds that assure the mating only of two individuals of the same species and thus prevent hybrids. All major traits of plants and animals are certainly adaptive or represent expressions of former adaptive traits. It was once believed that every inherited phenotypic characteristic of living organisms, no matter how small, was adaptive, but we know today that this is not always so.

Evolution

Evolution is the development of organisms through time. Basically it is the result of the differential survival in each generation of the progeny of individuals with certain special characteristics. In turn it is these adaptive characteristics that in part account for the differential survival. This last statement, like most generalizations, is a great simplification. Many and various other elements also play an important role.

First and foremost is the mechanism of inheritance. The ways in which genes determine the expression of characters in an organism and the manner in which genes are transmitted to the offspring shape the whole evolutionary picture. Evolution is often defined, and quite rightly so, as changes in the frequency of genes in a population. In turn the organization of genes in chromosomes and the behavior of these during cell division affect the mechanisms of inheritance and evolution.

Although evolution can take place without sexuality as known to us, this has not been the norm. Sexuality is a mechanism that tends to combine the genetic materials of individuals and produce new and novel combinations. Its effect is a tremendous increase in variability, and the advantages of this are so great that the phenomenon has become almost universal in all plants and animals. Sexuality apparently developed very early in the evolutionary history of organisms.

Without sexuality and interbreeding, species as we know them today would not exist. But just as important for the evolution, particularly the multiplication, of species has been the development of barriers to the free exchange of genes, be they geographical, ecological, behavioral, or genetical. The very simple earliest organisms may have been able to mix their genes with others of the same level of organization, but present-day organisms, with elaborate and complicated developmental pathways, cannot exchange genes with drastically different organisms. When they do the result of these exchanges is lethality or at best sterility. The selective advantage of barriers that prevent gene exchange in such instances is obvious. The fact that when we think and speak of evolution we refer almost always to the evolution of species is a clear indication of the important role of sexuality and isolation.

In a slightly different sense, it also can be said that evolution is shaped by the environment. Differential survival is always partly due to capacity to adapt to the environment, particularly the physical environment. Chemical evolution could occur only after our planet changed from the original "ball of fire" to a body where water could accumulate. Organic evolution, which has produced the tremendous number of organisms, is in part a consequence of the adaptation of these organisms to the infinite types of environments found on earth.

Evolution is then the result of the interplay of many and diverse factors. These factors themselves are subjected to change. Early in the history of each lineage of plants and animals, structures or processes have developed that have profoundly influenced the evolutionary history of that group. So, for example, a segmented body and an exoskeleton have been major factors in the success of the insects, but in turn these same factors have restricted the size and habits of the members of the class.

It is this multifaceted characteristic of evolutionary processes that makes the study of this subject so fascinating. And our knowledge is far from complete. Much remains to be discovered, much is to be learned. The application of new techniques, such as the use of high-speed digital computers, and the application of comparative biochemistry to elucidate developmental pathways or to discover evolutionary relationships at the chemical level promise to open grand new vistas in the field.

In the following chapters we will describe in detail some of the major evolutionary factors, analyze their role and relative importance, and investigate their development. We will also try to relate these factors to the field of taxonomy and the way man classifies organisms. Whenever possible we will attempt to point out how man's investigative tools, in this case the taxonomic system, limit as well as help in the acquisition of knowledge about nature. But first it might be useful to dispel some erroneous notions and popular misconceptions about evolution.

What Evolution Is Not

The misconceptions about evolution are many, and the reading of this account should hopefully dispel many of them. Nevertheless, two ideas are so fixed in the popular mind that they deserve to be considered separately. The first of them is the equation of evolution with struggle. The phrase "survival of the fittest" is Darwin's, but it is clear from his writings that he did not mean it literally. It was the British philosopher Herbert Spencer (1820–1903) who popularized the idea in his works and in his concept of social evolution. In the historical context of the times, the idea of struggle between individuals with the winner, the fittest, surviving to get the spoils was appealing to certain groups. This period represented the height of the laissez-faire era, the pinnacle of the British Empire. Spencer's ideas, with the apparent backing from the natural sciences, gave a supposed scientific (and, for some, moral) justification to the abuses of the times. In translating organic evolution to the social scene, Spencer misinterpreted the main idea—that is, differential survival of the progeny. He replaced it with one element of natural selection, differential mortality due to better adaptation to the environment, and interposed the idea of direct competition as responsible for differential mortality. The ideas as presented are entirely his, and have no scientific backing. Almost a hundred years later, the Soviet geneticist Lysenko, in the name of Darwinism and with the official blessing of the Communist party, was to denounce several aspects of modern genetics and cytology and accept the theory of the inheritance of acquired characters. In Stalinist Russia, these ideas gave an apparent scientific backing to the efforts of the state to mold the individual into an obedient servant, so that his descendants might become still more docile and obedient. In this case too, abandonment of scientific accuracy has created confusion, and while we are well aware of the fallacies and political motivations of Lysenko, we are not always so much aware of Spencer's mistakes.

We must keep always in mind that by the "fittest" Darwin meant the one with the largest surviving progeny. This can be and often is a comparatively weak individual. In this sense rabbits are "fitter" than lions, since they have been able to reproduce and occupy a larger area, in spite of man, than lions, which are fighting a losing battle against man. The comparison is not exactly accurate since the two animals do not occupy the same ecological niche nor do they have similar habits, but it illustrates the fact that physical strength or apparent supremacy is not necessarily automatically selected.

The second important point to understand is that no moral judgment of any sort can be read into evolution. Evolved organisms are not "better" in a moral sense, they are only better adapted to the environment they occupy compared to their extinct ancestors. We also should remember that every living species, by this very fact, is adapted to the environment it occupies presumably as effectively as any other living organism irrespective of their phylogenetic position. Evolution is as blind as Justice is supposed to be: those with the largest surviving progeny will multiply regardless of how good or bad humans may consider them.

Suggested Further Reading

Commoner, B. "DNA and the Chemistry of Inheritance." *American Scientist, 52*:365–388, 1964.

Darwin, C. *On the Origin of Species by Means of Natural Selection* (1859). Facsimile of the first edition with introduction by E. Mayr. Cambridge, Mass.: Harvard University Press, 1964.

Dobzhansky, T. "What Is an Adaptive Trait?" *American Naturalist, 90*:337–347, 1956.

Dobzhansky, T. *Mankind Evolving: The Evolution of the Human Species.* New Haven, Conn.: Yale University Press, 1962 (particularly Chapters 1–3).

Gaffron, H. "The Origin of Life." In S. Tax (ed.), *Evolution After Darwin,* Vol. I. Chicago: University of Chicago Press, 1960.

Huxley, J. *Soviet Genetics and World Science: Lysenko and the Meaning of Heredity.* London: Chatto and Windus, 1949, (interesting account of the "Lysenko" controversy).

Irvine, W. *Apes, Angels, and Victorians.* New York: Meridian Books, 1959 (historical background on Darwin and his time).

Shapley, H. "Crusted Stars and Self-Warming Planets." *The American Scholar, 31:*512–515, 1962.

Sheppard, P. M. *Natural Selection and Heredity.* London: Hutchinson University Library, 1958.

Simpson, G. G. *The Meaning of Evolution.* New Haven, Conn.: Yale University Press, 1949.

Sonneborn, T. M. (ed.). *The Control of Human Heredity and Evolution.* New York: The Macmillan Company, 1965 (some ideas about the future).

Inheritance and the Sources of Variation

EVOLUTION IS DEPENDENT UPON the transmission to the offspring of the characteristics that account for the success of the parents. Were it not so, differential survival would not have any effect on the kinds of organisms that form the next generation. In effect, the offspring of a successful animal or plant might be eliminated on account of lack of the successful characters of its parents.

Darwin realized that inheritance played an important role in evolution. He was very much interested in the mechanisms underlying inheritance and reproduction, and conducted many experiments to learn about them. But he was never able to solve the basic problems, and genetics is the weak aspect of the original enunciation of the theory of evolution.

Particulate and Blending Inheritance

A common observation is that a particular offspring is not an exact copy of its parents, sometimes resembling one parent more than the other or occasionally resembling a more remote ancestor. Some are found to have entirely new attributes. Over the years elaborate theories have been brought forth to explain these observations. So, for example, it has been proposed that the characteristics of certain parts of the plant or animal were inherited exclusively from the maternal line, while other attributes came from the paternal line. The seasons of the year have been suspected of causing certain characteristics. Foods ingested by the mother have been proposed as the basis for certain effects on the offspring, and so on. At the base of all these ideas lay the concept that heredity somehow consisted of a mythical "mixing of the bloods" of the ancestors. This notion still persists in popular thought and is reflected in our language in expressions such as calling a purebred animal a "pure blood" or in sayings that a person has his father's or mother's "blood." This theory of inheritance is known as blending inheritance. According to it, the totality of the characters of both parents are transmitted as a unit to the offspring, where they mix and lose their individuality. The fact that the offspring has a different aspect than either of its parents is supposed to be due to this mixing effect; differences among siblings are explained by assigning variable strength to the

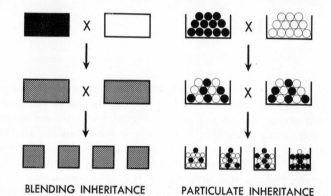

BLENDING INHERITANCE   PARTICULATE INHERITANCE

Figure 2·1. Effect of blending and particulate inheritance on variability. When crossing two extremes, under blending inheritance all the offspring of coming generations is intermediate; under particulate inheritance there will be segregation after the first generation. The observed situation is the second.

"humors" of the parents. An often cited further justification of blending inheritance is that the characteristics of the offspring tend to be in between those of the parents.

This last corollary has an important evolutionary consequence. Natural populations of plants and animals are formed by individuals that are not alike in their characteristics. This furnishes the raw material for natural selection. But under the theory of blending inheritance this necessary variability would be drastically curtailed, and in a very few generations the members of a population would be completely uniform in all their characteristics (Figure 2·1). No more evolution would be possible unless a new source of variability were introduced. Since no such drastic homogenization is observed in nature, the proponents of the blending theory of heredity postulated a rate of mutation that was equivalent to the loss of variability due to blending. The mechanism by which variability was introduced was believed to be the inheritance of acquired characters.

Charles Darwin was aware that a store of variability in a population was necessary for natural selection to act upon and thus bring about evolution. In a population where all individuals are exactly alike, obviously nothing is changed from generation to generation, even in the case when there is differential reproduction. In his travels around the world, and in his observations on the flora and fauna of his native England, Darwin had realized that animal and plant populations are not uniform but quite variable. Furthermore his extensive breeding experiments with plants had shown him that this variability was inherited and not due to accidents of the environment. Evolution through natural selection required the presence of a large store of variability, but under the theory of blending inheritance, almost universally accepted at the time, variability should be practically nonexistant within a breeding population. Darwin tried to reconcile this conflict by providing his theory of Panmixis. It stated that representative particles, pangenes, coming from all parts of the body and carrying information on inherited and acquired characteristics are incorporated into the gametes and transmitted to the offspring. This complicated theory could never be verified experimentally, and furthermore it did not explain all of the observed facts. It was never quite accepted.

We know today that the correct solution to the problem is particulate inheritance. It was the Austrian monk Gregor Mendel who proposed this theory. According to it, parents transmit to their offspring particles, now called genes, that carry the necessary information to reproduce the characteristics of the parents. The genes are blueprints for the development of a character. Since the offspring receives an equal number of genes from the paternal and maternal lines, in sexually reproducing organisms there will be at least two of each kind of genes affecting the same character, although each of them will not necessarily affect it the same way. Such genes are called alleles.

Genes are located on structures called chromosomes, a particular gene always being located in the same precise position on the chromosome, called the locus (Latin for "place," plural "loci") of the gene. Allelic genes therefore occupy the same locus on their respective chromosomes. The number of possible alleles can vary for a certain gene from one to many. Each individual can have not more than two at a time, one received from the father and one from the mother. If two alleles of a particular gene inherited by an individual are different, known as heterozygosity, the offspring may express only one of them, referred to then as the dominant allele, or it may express an intermediate condition. It is the combination of dominance at some loci and intermediate situations at others that in part accounts for the similarities and differences between the parents and their offspring. If in a population there is only one allele for each of the genes affecting a character, all of the members of the population will possess that same character.

Particulate inheritance, or Mendelian inheritance as it is often called, incorporates three main concepts:

1. Inheritance is particulate and discrete, and each parent contributes to its offspring an equal amount, with the exception of those animals and plants that have sex chromosomes, in which case the contribution of only these chromosomes is unequal. The inheritable particles are the genes. The existence of genes has been deduced theoretically but they have not been identified with certainty. Nevertheless we know that there are probably more than one "kind" of gene and that they are part of a giant DNA molecule.

2. Although some genes may suppress, mask, or alter the effects of other genes, the inherited factors do not contaminate one another —that is, the genes are not changed or altered in their fundamental structure, and they will be transmitted to the next generation in the same form in which they were received.

3. The genes are exceptionally stable in their composition and function. Nevertheless they can change, or mutate, to a different form called a mutant, in which case their function is also altered. Genes can mutate due to ever present natural causes, in which case the action is called spontaneous mutation, or they may mutate as a result of artificially applied outside agents such as certain chemicals or certain radiations, particularly x-rays (and man-made atmospheric radiation, resulting from atomic fallout!). Substances capable of inducing mutations are called mutagens, and this type of mutation is called induced mutation, although the difference, if any, between natural and induced mutation is not very clear.

Mendel proposed two main corollaries to his theory that are commonly called "Mendel's laws of inheritance." The first of these is the law of segregation. Stated in modern terminology, it says that if two individuals, called the parental generation (P), differing by one gene are crossed to each other, and if the progeny or first filial generation (F_1) is mated to itself, its progeny, or second filial generation (F_2), will consist of three types of individuals in the following proportion: one-fourth will resemble one of the grandparents (P), one-half will resemble the parent (F_1), and one-fourth will resemble the other grandparent (P) (Figure 2·2). In those cases where complete dominance is present in the first filial generation (F_1)—that is, when only one of the two alleles is expressed—

the class in the F_2 that resembles the F_1 will not be distinguishable morphologically from the class representing the dominant grandparent. In such cases the proportion in the F_2 is three-fourths like the dominant grandparent and one-fourth like the other grandparent, called the recessive in such case, or, as it is usually noted, a 3:1 ratio. The law of segregation has been demonstrated many times, and is a logical corollary of the stability of genes as discussed above. The law of segregation also helps to explain why often a character in some of the offspring does not resemble either parent, but is more like one of the grandparents.

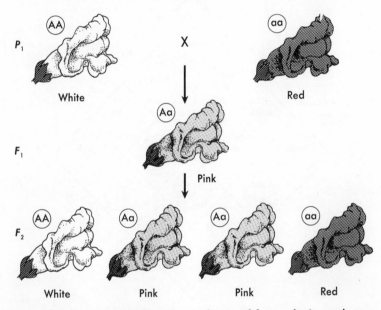

Figure 2·2. Mendel's law of segregation. In the case of flower color in snapdragons, there is no dominance, the F_1 being intermediate between the parents—that is, pink.

The second Mendelian law is known as the law of independent assortment. It states simply that two or more nonallelic genes present in the parental generation (P) will segregate in the F_2 completely independently of each other (Figure 2·3). Contrary to what is true for the law of segregation, we know that in many cases there is no independent assortment, due to the phenomenon of linkage, to be discussed in Chapter 4. Nevertheless independent assortment is important, and changes increasing or decreasing the amount of linkage, have played a major role in the formation of species and in their subsequent evolution

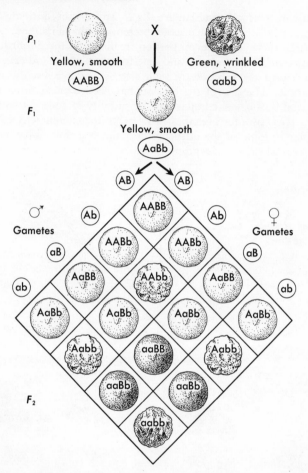

Figure 2·3. Mendel's law of independent assortment. Note that the segregation of yellow versus green color in peas is independent from smooth versus wrinkled surface. In this case there is dominance, the F_1 being as one parent—that is, yellow and smooth.

Single Genes and Multiple Gene Systems

Although there are instances where a character of an organism is controlled by a single gene, the great majority of cases are much more complex. Most, if not all, characteristics of an organism are determined by more than one gene. These genes can have a drastic effect on the character, or they can have an effect so slight that it cannot ordinarily be seen. Furthermore, there is hardly a gene that affects only one character; most genes affect different parts and functions of the organism, although their major action may be evident only in a particular structure or time of development. This might seem to contradict what has been said about particulate inheritance. How can every gene that is supposed to store some precise piece of information affect so many aspects of a plant's or an animal's life? This apparent puzzle can be better comprehended if the way a gene works is understood.

A gene is like a blueprint in the formation of amino acids. Amino acids are the building blocks of complex proteins called enzymes. The enzymes act as catalysts—that is, they accelerate certain reactions within the cell. Enzymes are specific, catalyzing only a particular kind of chemical reaction in the cell. But to produce a flower or a limb, even a hair or color in a petal, a whole set of complex chemical reactions are needed, each of them catalyzed by a specific enzyme produced by a particular gene or set of genes (Figure 2·4). But most of the chemical reactions taking place in the cells during development of an insect wing, for example, are not unique to that structure, only their timing and relative importance and rates are probably unique. It can then easily be seen how more than one gene is involved in the development of a character, and how a gene can affect more than one character.[1]

If the effect of a gene is minor, its presence or absence will produce only a minor effect, and if we measure the character, the variation between an organism not having the gene and those having one or two genes will be minor. The same applies when a series of different, nonallelic genes affect a character. In such a case, the variation within a population appears to be continuous between the two extremes. Systems of genes that individually have small cumulative effects and together control continuous variation are called multiple gene systems; genes that individually have drastic effects and produce discontinuous effects are called major or, sometimes, Mendelian genes.

There is no absolute distinction between multiple gene systems and major genes, since groups of genes with all degrees of intermediate effects are known. Moreover, a gene may drastically affect one character and be classified as a major gene, and only slightly affect another and consequently be also classed as part of a multiple

[1] The nature and action of the units of heredity (cistrons, regulator genes, operons, and so on) at the subcellular and cellular level are now fairly well understood. The use of the general term "gene" is nevertheless justified in explaining genetic phenomena at the populational level where our knowledge of gene action is still incomplete.

gene system. Nevertheless, despite the absence of a clear distinction between major genes and systems of multiple genes, the latter concept is useful and quite adequate for most purposes.

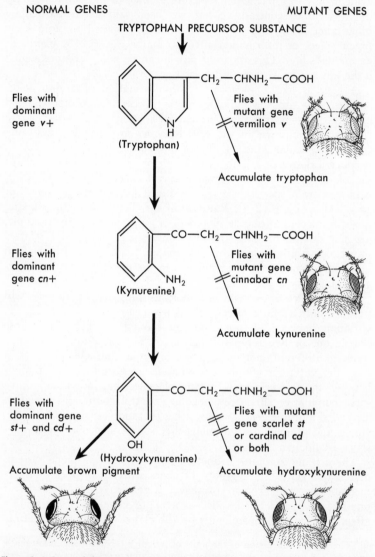

NORMAL GENES   MUTANT GENES

TRYPTOPHAN PRECURSOR SUBSTANCE

Flies with dominant gene v+

CH_2—$CHNH_2$—$COOH$

(Tryptophan)

Flies with mutant gene vermilion v

Accumulate tryptophan

Flies with dominant gene cn+

CO—CH_2—$CHNH_2$—$COOH$

NH_2

(Kynurenine)

Flies with mutant gene cinnabar cn

Accumulate kynurenine

Flies with dominant gene st+ and cd+

CO—CH_2—$CHNH_2$—$COOH$

OH

(Hydroxykynurenine)

Accumulate brown pigment

Flies with mutant gene scarlet st or cardinal cd or both

Accumulate hydroxykynurenine

Figure 2·4. Some of the steps involved in the formation of the brown eye pigment in *Drosophila*, and the genes that control them. At left, the normal situation; at right, the action of the mutant genes. Although the obvious effect is a morphological one, the genes act by affecting specific chemical reactions in the cell.

It might be thought that a character such as height, which varies continuously in a population, or color intensity, with all kinds of gradations between the lightest and the darkest, could not be controlled by particulate genes having defined and distinct effects. Major genes certainly cannot produce such an effect, but a large number of genes, each with a small cumulative effect, can. This was first demonstrated in 1911 by the Swedish geneticist Nilsson-Ehle. Working with wheat, he discovered three nonallelic factors that affected the color of the kernels. Plants that were double recessive for all three factors had white kernels; plants with all dominant factors had dark red kernels; kernels of plants with some, but not all, dominant factors were also red but not so dark. The action of each gene was similar to that of the others. When each plant was studied independently, plants homozygous for two factors and heterozygous for one produced a ratio of 3 red: 1 white kernels; plants heterozygous for two genes produced a 15:1 ratio; and plants heterozygous for all three gave a 63:1 ratio. When the red kernels of the F_2 plants that combined all three factors were grown, some plants segregated in a 3:1 ratio, others in a 15:1 ratio, and still others in a 63:1 ratio. It is clear that each gene behaves as a true Mendelian factor and that they follow the first and second Mendelian laws. But obviously the effect of the three factors is additive, which is further borne out by variations in the intensity of the red kernels. Series of such genes then, each with a small effect, account for the inheritance of quantitative characters with a seemingly continuous variation.

Nevertheless, even when more than one factor is involved, there still ought to be some discontinuity, although there might be some problem in distinguishing the classes. Another factor complicates matters further. This is the noninheritable component of variation —that is, the effects of such environmental factors as food, temperature, light, shelter. These factors produce variation that is noninheritable. A well-fed animal will be heavier and possibly bigger than an undernourished one of the same genetic composition. Since its offspring will not be any heavier than those of the undernourished one when both are fed the same amount, this component does not play any major evolutionary role. In order to avoid this environmental effect the geneticist tries to grow his plants and animals in uniform environments. But it is almost never possible in a field to avoid small variations in such things as rainfall, drainage, minerals in the soil. Therefore the combination of many discrete genes affecting a character, each in a small degree, and environmental noninheritable changes is what produces truly continuous variation.

The Hardy-Weinberg Law and the Maintenance of Variation

The importance of variability in evolution can hardly be over-emphasized. Unless members of a population are different, selection cannot operate. The sources of variation are two: genetic and nongenetic. For evolution, only the first is of importance. We have already seen that continuous as well as discontinuous variation have exactly the same genetic basis. But natural selection by favoring some individuals (and the genes they carry) over others (which eventually may be totally eliminated from the population) tends to decrease the variability. Consequently it has to be replenished constantly. The source of new variability is gene mutation. In addition there is immigration of individuals with novel genetic material from neighboring populations; and finally there is the production of new types as the result of recombination of genes due to the sexual process in the population.

The exclusiveness of selection as the agent of change in evolution has been questioned occasionally, particularly by the proponents of the theory of orthogenesis, which maintain that some internal "driving force" tends to modify the frequency of the genes in a population.

Particulate inheritance offers a model that explains the transmission of individual characteristics without loss of variability. A mathematical corollary was pointed out independently in 1908 by G. H. Hardy, a British mathematician, and G. Weinberg, a German geneticist, which is known as the Hardy-Weinberg law. This law demonstrates that the original variability will be maintained in the population in the absence of forces that tend to decrease (selection) or increase (mutation, gene flow) this variability.

Let us consider a population formed by a very large number of individuals (theoretically infinitely large) and where breeding is strictly random. Suppose that A_1 and A_2 are a pair of genes present with a frequency p and q respectively, such that $p + q = 1$. These two genes combining at random will produce the following genotypes with the following frequencies:

$$A_1A_1: \quad p \times p = p^2$$
$$A_1A_2: \quad p \times q$$
$$A_2A_1: \quad q \times p$$
$$A_2A_2: \quad q \times q = q^2$$

Since genetically A_1A_2 and A_2A_1 are identical, their combined frequency is $2 \times p \times q$.

In the next generation the homozygous genotypes will produce only one kind of gamete, while the heterozygous genotypes will produce both kinds of gametes in equal numbers. If each organism in the population on the average produces the same number of gametes, the proportion of each kind will depend on the frequency of the different genotypes in the population, so that:

proportion of A_1 gametes: $p^2 + \frac{1}{2} \times 2 \times p \times q = p(p + q) = p$

proportion of A_2 gametes: $q^2 + \frac{1}{2} \times 2 \times p \times q = q(q + p) = q$

The frequency of A_1 and A_2 gametes produced by the population after one generation of random mating without selection or mutation is the same as that of the gametes that gave rise to it. It follows that the proportion of genotypes in subsequent generations is not going to change either, and consequently the initial variability has been maintained.

The Hardy-Weinberg law demonstrates that the initial variability in a population will be maintained and that any changes in the frequency of genes are brought about by outside forces. No explanation, such as the inheritance of acquired characters, is needed to explain the observed variability. Essentially the Hardy-Weinberg law demonstrates the compatibility between Mendelian genetics and Darwinian evolution.

Suggested Further Reading

Beadle, G. W. "Structure of the Genetic Material and the Concept of the Gene." In W. H. Johnson and W. C. Steere (eds.), *This Is Life*.

Grant, V. *The Architecture of the Germplasm*. New York: John Wiley & Sons, 1964, 236 pp. (particularly Chapters 1–5).

Hardy, G. W. "Mendelian Proportions in a Mixed Population." *Science*, 28:49–50. Reproduced in J. A. Peters, *Classical Papers in Genetics*. Englewood Cliffs, N.J.: Prentice-Hall, 1961, pp. 60–62.

Levine, R. P. *Genetics*. Modern Biology Series. New York: Holt, Reinholdt, & Winston, 1962, 180 pp.

Sinnott, E. W., L. C. Dunn, and T. Dobzhansky. *Principles of Genetics*. New York: McGraw-Hill Book Co., 1950, 498 pp.

3

Evolution at the Population Level

FROM A GENETIC POINT OF VIEW, evolution is the change in the frequency of the genes of a population. Genes that do not contribute to the survival of the individual carrying them will tend to be eliminated; those that do will become more numerous. Through mutation and the introduction of genes from neighboring populations new genes are constantly being added to the population. The sexual mechanism in turn shuffles and reshuffles the genes of the population into novel recombinations. Some of these will prove superior and produce more of their kind, while others will tend to disappear. The interplay of all these factors produces changes in the frequency of genes and hence evolution.

The Hardy-Weinberg law, introduced in Chapter 2, demonstrates that in a large, randomly mating population, no changes occur in the absence of mutation and selection. But mutation and selection are universally present in natural populations. Let us then briefly review the dynamics of the forces that account for the changes in gene frequency.

Mutation

Certain kinds of mutations are so rare as to be virtually unique. They do not have any permanent effect on the population because they have an infinitely small chance of survival in a large population, unless they give a very great and immediate advantage to their carriers, a highly improbable event. Other types of mutations, on the other hand, called recurrent mutations, occur with a measurable frequency. They do have a very important effect, one that can be predicted mathematically.

Let us consider a gene A_1 which mutates to A_2, and let us indicate by u the rate or frequency at which A_1 mutates to A_2. This rate varies according to the gene and the organism, but it is usually of the order of 10^{-4} to 10^{-8} (that is, as many as one A_2 mutation in 10,000 to as few as one per 100,000,000 A_1 genes in each generation). If the frequency of A_1 is p_o, the frequency of the newly mutated genes A_2 in the following generation will be $A_1 - A_2$, or $p_o - u \times p_o$, and consequently the change in the frequency of A_1 will be $- u \times p_o$.

If we imagine that there were 1,000,000 gametes containing the A_1 gene, and that the rate at which they mutated to A_2 was $u = 10^{-4}$ (1/10,000), the following numerical values can be calculated:

$$p_o = 1 \text{ (all genes were } A_1 \text{)}; \; u \times p_o = 1 \times 10^{-4}, \text{ or } 0.0001$$

and the new frequency of A_1: $p_o - u \times p_o = 1 - 0.0001 = 0.9999$.

After one generation, there will be 999,900 gametes with the gene A_1 and 100 with the gene A_2.

But the new gene A_2 can mutate back to A_1, a phenomenon called back mutation. If we indicate by v the rate at which A_2 mutates to A_1, and apply the same reasoning used to calculate the changes accompanying the mutation of A_1 to A_2, we have:

initial gene frequency of A_1 and A_2: p_o and q_o

$$\text{mutation rates: } A_1 \overset{u}{\underset{v}{\rightleftarrows}} A_2$$

changes in frequency: $p_o - u \times p_o;\; q_o - v \times q_o$

and considering both events, the total change in the frequency p of the gene A_1 is:

$$\Delta q = u \times p_o - v \times q_o.$$

As the frequency of one allele increases, fewer of the other are left to mutate in that direction, and more are available to mutate back to the original type. Eventually an equilibrium will be reached, at which point no further frequency changes will take place as a result of mutation. The point of equilibrium is found by equating the change of frequency q to zero (when both rates are at equilibrium no changes occur). Thus at equilibrium:

$$p \times u = q \times v, \text{ or } \frac{p}{q} = \frac{v}{u},$$

and adding q to both sides of the equation and solving,

$$q = \frac{u}{u + v}$$

We see that the frequency of the gene A_1 depends exclusively (in the absence of selection) on the rate at which it mutates to A_2 and on the rate at which A_2 mutates back to A_1. Since these rates are very low (the rate of back mutations is usually only about one-tenth of the mutation rate), the change that mutation alone introduces into a population (at Hardy-Weinberg equilibrium, and in the absence of selection) is very low. At the normal mutation rates it will take from a minimum of 5,000 to a maximum of more than 50,000,000 generations, to replace half of the A_1 genes by A_2 genes in a population. From this we can see that the effect of mutation is greater, the shorter the span of each generation. In man, 50,000 generations means 1,000,000 to 2,000,000 years, but in a bacterium with a very fast generation time, let us say half an hour, the same number of generations can elapse in less than three years. We also see that whenever the rate of mutation is larger than that of back mutation, the mutant will replace the original gene unless selected against, as is the usual case. A final conclusion can be drawn. Increases in the rate of mutation will not produce any changes unless they affect the rate of mutation and back mutation in different ways. Otherwise the original equilibrium as given by the formula will not change.

Recombination

This term refers to the mixing in the offspring of the gene contents of the chromosomes of their parents. Recombination is important for two main reasons: basically, because the different genes of a plant or animal interact and certain combinations of genes are better than others; and secondly, because the number of recombinants is infinitely larger than the possible number of mutations. Although the ultimate source of new genetic information comes from mutation, most "new" types in a population arise by recombination. This process can produce more, and more varied, types and at a faster rate than can mutation, and recombination rather than mutation is the immediate source of variability in a population. Sexuality is the outward manifestation of the modifications that have taken place in the phenotype to assure recombination. Recombination takes place when the nuclei and the chromosomes of a male and female gamete fuse to form the nucleus of the zygote (for more details see Chapter 4).

If a heterozygous organism that produces large numbers of offspring, of the constitution $A_1A_2 \, B_1B_2$ is crossed with another of its same constitution, the offspring (in the absence of linkage between the two loci—see next chapter) will be of the following constitution (according to Mendel's second law) :

$$A_1A_1B_1B_1; \; A_1A_1B_1B_2; \; A_1A_1B_2B_2; \; A_1A_2B_1B_1; \; A_1A_2B_1B_2;$$

$$A_1A_2B_2B_2; \; A_2A_2B_1B_1; \; A_2A_2B_1B_2; \; A_2A_2B_2B_2$$

altogether nine different types. Each of these types can arise by mutation, but the chances that all nine types arise by mutation in one generation is very small, so small that it is virtually impossible (considering the rate of mutation to be equal to 10^{-4}, the probability in a population of obtaining these nine types in one generation is 10^{-24}, or 1 in a billion billion!).

The number of diploid genotypes that can be assembled from any number of alleles of a gene is given by the following formula:

$$g = \frac{r(r+1)}{2}$$

where g = number of diploid genotypes, and r = the number of alleles at any one locus.

If we now consider two different loci, which are in different chromosomes so that they can be freely recombined, the total number of possible diploid genotypes that can be assembled for two genes considered together is:

$$g_A \times g_B = \frac{r(r+1)}{2} \times \frac{r(r+1)}{2} = \left[\frac{r(r+1)}{2} \right]^2$$

For example, if we consider that at each of the two loci there are two alleles, $r = 2$; $g_A \times g_B = \left[\dfrac{2(2+1)}{2} \right]^2 = 9$, which as we saw above is the number of possible combinations when we recombine two organisms differing at two loci with two alleles in each.

If instead of dealing with two genes we are concerned with three, the number of recombinations is given by the product of $g_A \times g_B \times g_C$, and so on, so that for n genes the number of recombinants will be:

$$g_A \times g_B \times g_C \times \cdots \times g_n = \frac{r(r+1)}{2} \times \frac{r(r+1)}{2} \times \cdots \times \frac{r(r+1)}{2}$$

$$= \left[\frac{r(r+1)}{2} \right]^n$$

The number of possible recombinations depends then on the number of alleles at a locus (r) and on the number of independent loci (n), and it is quite high whenever r and n are over 3, as is the usual case. So for example, for $n = 10$ and $r = 3$, the value is $6^{10} = 60,466,176$. And the number of genes in each organism is not 10 but is probably in the order of 10,000! It is clear that the variability obtained by recombination is very high, so high that a series of mechanisms have evolved to control and restrict recombination.

Recombination by itself does not produce any change in genetic information but uncovers arrangements of genes on which selection can act by favoring some and eliminating others. Let us now look at the way selection operates in a population to bring these changes about.

Selection

We have seen already that natural selection is the process that accounts for the differential contribution of offspring to the next generation. The proportionate contribution is sometimes also called fitness or adaptive value. The number of offspring an organism contributes to the next generation depends on a series of factors. Most populations of plants and animals tend to go through cycles of expansion and shrinkage. When the population is expanding, most individuals will probably produce some surviving descendants; when the population is shrinking, few will. But at every instance some individuals will be producing a proportionately greater number of surviving offspring than others. To be able to study selection at all stages and over several generations, one must therefore consider frequencies rather than absolute numbers. Furthermore, to compare the effect of selection on different members of a population, selection is supposed to be always acting against rather than in favor of the offspring of a certain organism.

In sexually reproducing plants and animals the genic makeup of the offspring differs from that of either of its parents. Consequently it is simpler to study the effect of selection on genes rather than on organisms. By convention the fitness of the gene transmitted to the next generation with the highest frequency is fixed at 1, regardless of the actual number of surviving offspring that carry the gene. Nevertheless, it should clearly be understood that selection operates on individual organisms, and only through them on genes. Only when the differences in fitness between individuals are associated with the presence or absence of a particular gene or group of genes in the individual's genotype does selection operate on that gene, and the genotype that contains it. Consequently the product of selection that affects evolution is determined by the way all of the genes together affect the fitness of an organism.

Most, if not all, new mutations reduce the fitness of the individuals that carry them in a homozygous condition. Many mutations are lethal when homozygous, which means that individuals with a double dose of that gene die. Other mutations are semilethal; most individuals carrying a double dose die but some survive. And finally other mutations are subvital; the fitness of the individuals homozygous for it is reduced but not drastically. In a heterozygous condition, on the other hand, lethal, sublethal, and subvital genes can reduce the fitness of their carriers, be completely neutral (recessive), or even increase the fitness of their carriers. In the first case, there is no dominance for fitness; in the second, recessiveness is complete (since the action of the mutant gene is completely masked); and in the third case, it is an overdominant or heterotic gene. Obviously the behavior of the gene in both the homozygous and heterozygous condition determines its selective advantage or disadvantage in the population. It should be remembered that when a mutation first appears it will be in a heterozygous condition; its early fate will depend on its effect in this condition. Only when it has become more frequent (as a result of favorable selection) will it become homozygous in some individuals.

Before proceeding to study these cases in detail, it is convenient to remember also that the genes in the chromosomes of an individual interact with each other, and that the fitness of a particular gene to a certain extent depends on the other genes. So, for example, certain genes are completely recessive in certain genotypes but deleterious in other genotypes. Consequently, when we assign a certain fitness to a particular gene, this refers to the average fitness of that gene in the whole population.

We will first study the changes in the frequency of a gene A_2 brought about by selection when there is complete dominance—that is, when the mutant form is selected against only when it is in a homozygous state, since when it is in a heterozygous condition it has no effect whatsoever on fitness (complete dominance). We know from Chapter 2 (Hardy-Weinberg law) that the frequencies of the three possible combinations between two alleles are:

$$A_1A_1 = p^2, \ A_1A_2 = 2 \ pq, \ A_2A_2 = q^2,$$

and that

$$p^2 + 2pq + q^2 = 1$$

The fitness of these combinations by definition is in this case:

$$A_1A_1 = 1, \ A_1A_2 = 1, \ \text{and} \ A_2A_2 = 1 - s$$

where s represents the coefficient of selection against homozygous recessives. The gametic contribution therefore will be:

$$A_1A_1 = p^2 \times 1, \ A_1A_2 = 2pq \times 1, \ A_2A_2 = q^2 \times (1 - s)$$

since the gametic contribution is equal to the product of the frequency times the coefficient of selection. The total contribution will no longer be unity, but $1 - sq^2$. In order to find out the frequency of A_2 genes in the next generation, we have to add one-half of the contribution of A_1A_2 plus the contribution of A_2A_2 and divide by the new total, so that the frequency of A_2 in generation 1 is

$$q_1 = \frac{q^2 (1 - s) + pq}{1 - sq^2}$$

The change that has resulted in one generation as the result of selection is:

$$\Delta q = q_1 - q$$
$$= \frac{q^2 (1 - s) + pq}{1 - sq^2} - q,$$

which on simplification reduces to

$$= -\frac{sq^2 (1 - q)}{1 - sq^2}$$

The same type of reasoning is applied to calculate the effects of selection when selection works against a dominant gene A_1 rather than the recessive A_2; or when selection affects A_2 both when homozygous or heterozygous; or when there is overdominance and both genes A_1 and A_2, are selected against when homozygous. The resulting formulas are shown in Table $3 \cdot 1$.

TABLE 3·1

Change of Gene Frequency, Δq, after One Generation of Selection Under Different Conditions of Dominance

CONDITIONS OF DOMINANCE AND SELECTION	INITIAL FREQUENCIES AND FITNESS OF THE GENOTYPES			CHANGE OF FREQUENCY Δq, OF GENE A_2
	A_1A_1 p^2	A_1A_2 $2pq$	A_2A_2 q^2	
No dominance selection against A_2	1	$1-\frac{1}{2}s$	$1-s$	$\dfrac{-\frac{1}{2}sq\,(1-q)}{1-sq}$
Complete dominance selection against A_2A_2	1	1	$1-s$	$\dfrac{-sq^2\,(1-q)}{1-sq^2}$
Complete dominance selection against A_1	$1-s$	$1-s$	1	$\dfrac{+sq^2\,(1-q)}{1-s\,(1-q^2)}$
Overdominance selection against A_1A_1 and A_2A_2	$1-s_1$	1	$1-s_2$	$\dfrac{+pq\,(s_1p-s_2q)}{1-s_1p^2-s_2q^2}$

When s is small the denominators differ little from 1, and the numerators alone can be taken to represent Δq sufficiently accurately for most purposes.

Source: From Table $2 \cdot 1$ in D. S. Falconer, *Introduction to Quantitative Genetics*, published by Oliver & Boyd Ltd., Edinburgh, and used by permission of the author and publishers.

From the formulas in Table $3 \cdot 1$ several conclusions can be drawn. First of all, we see that selection depends on the coefficient of selection s, and on the initial frequencies q, or p and q, in the cases where overdominance is present. The relationship is not a simple one, but a rather complex one. From the formulas in Table $3 \cdot 1$ and the graphs in Figure $3 \cdot 1$, it can be seen that selection is most effective when the gene is at an intermediate frequency, and becomes least effective when the mutant is at a very high or very low frequency. Furthermore, selection against a recessive mutant is highly ineffective when that mutant is at a low frequency. This is due to the fact that in such circumstances it will be found largely or entirely in heterozygous combinations, where it is "shielded" from selection.

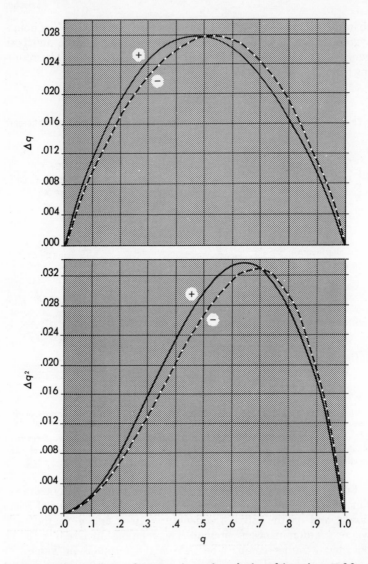

Figure 3·1. Change of gene frequency Δq, under selection of intensity $s = 0.2$, at different values of initial frequency q. Upper figure shows a gene with no dominance; lower figure shows a gene with complete dominance. The graphs marked ($-$) refer to selection against the gene whose frequency is q, so that Δq is negative. The graphs marked ($+$) refer to selection in favor of the gene, so that Δq is positive. [From Figure 2·2 in D. S. Falconer, *Introduction to Quantitative Genetics*, published by Oliver & Boyd Ltd., Edinburgh, and used by permission of the author and publishers.]

As we have seen before, when the frequency of the original gene is high (and that of the mutant is low), mutation is most effective, since there are more genes that can mutate ($p \times u$), which coincides with the conditions at which selection is most ineffective. But as the frequency of the mutant form increases, selection becomes more effective and mutation less so, until an equilibrium is reached.

Let us consider the situation where the mutant is selected against only in the homozygous situation. At equilibrium the changes produced in one generation by mutation should equal those brought about by selection, so that:

$$u \times p - v \times q = \frac{sq^2 (1 - q)}{1 - sq^2}$$

$$u (1 - q) - v \times q = \frac{sq^2 (1 - q)}{1 - sq^2}$$

We can simplify this equation, sacrificing some accuracy but not too much, in order to get a better understanding of the relationships. First we can simplify the equation by disregarding the back mutations ($- v \times q$), which are almost negligible when the frequency of A_2 is low, and we can further disregard the denominator $1 - sq^2$, since its value is near unity when the frequency of A_2 is low. The simplified equation then becomes:

$$u (1 - q) = sq^2 (1 - q)$$

$$u = sq^2$$

$$q = \sqrt{\frac{u}{s}}$$

(approximate)

This approximate expression for the gene frequencies of the mutant gene A_2, when mutation and selection are at equilibrium, indicates that the equilibrium frequency of the gene A_2 will depend on the relative values of the mutation rate and the coefficient of selection, and theoretically at least, the equilibrium frequency could have many different values. But given the normally low values of mutation (in the order of 10^{-4} to 10^{-8}), the frequency of the mutant will be kept at low values even without too great a selection against it. It is clear therefore that the joint action of selection and mutation should keep deleterious mutants that have no heterotic effects at a low frequency, a fact confirmed by observations on natural populations. A further conclusion is that mutation alone is not a likely cause of evolutionary change, and it is selection that chiefly determines whether a gene spreads through the population or remains a rarity.

Gene Flow

Mutation and selection are phenomena that occur within the population and are not dependent on events occurring elsewhere. Mutation is a random phenomenon that introduces genetic variability at a slow but steady rate, while selection is the conservative and leveling force that tends to standardize all the individuals of a population at a peak of maximum fitness. Inasmuch as most mutations decrease fitness, these two forces work against each other as we have just seen.

Gene flow is the introduction of new genes into a population from outside sources, usually contiguous populations, in the form of occasional crosses between individuals of different breeding populations, incorporation of an animal born elsewhere, or introduction of foreign seed or pollen. In all these cases, genes derived by mutation and maintained by selection in a different environment are introduced into the population. The immediate effect is similar to the effect of mutation; a new source of variability is introduced. If we consider that a population receives each generation a number of immigrants, and that the immigrants possess a gene C_2 at frequency q_m instead of the gene C_1, after gene flow the population will have a frequency, m, of immigrants, and $1 - m$ of native individuals. The frequency q_0 of the gene C_1 will have changed to the new frequency q_1 in the following way:

$$q_1 = mq_m + (1 - m)\, q_o$$
$$= m\,(q_m - q_o) + q_o$$

The change Δq in the frequency of C_1 brought about by gene flow is the difference between the initial frequency q_o and the frequency q_1 after gene flow has taken place:

$$\Delta q = q_1 - q_o$$
$$= m\,(q_m - q_o) + q_o - q_o = m\,(q_m - q_o)$$

Thus the change of gene frequency brought about by gene flow depends on the number of immigrants (m), the initial frequency q_o of C_1, and the frequency q_m of C_2 in the immigrants.

But gene flow has broader implications that are best understood if we consider the nature of the genes that are introduced. Inasmuch as the immigrants represent random samples of their original populations, they will carry in a high frequency genes that are favorable there, and very infrequently they will introduce deleterious genes, since, as we have already seen, they are kept at a low frequency by selection. Now, genes that increase the fitness of individuals of population A do not necessarily increase the fitness of individuals of population B, due to different genetic backgrounds and to different selection pressures in the two populations. But they seldom are very deleterious, particularly when they come from neighboring populations that have only small genetic and environmental differences. Consequently the intensity of selection against these factors will not be great. Genes introduced through gene flow are eliminated at a low rate. Furthermore, a relatively high proportion (compared to genes arising by mutation) of the genes acquired through gene flow have a beneficial effect, and they will tend to become established. In certain cases, they play a very important role, particularly when different species form hybrids, as we shall see further on.

The net effect of gene flow is that of a cohesive force that works counter to selection without affecting fitness to any great extent, but which hinders populations of the same species from becoming very different. Since the effect of gene flow is directly related to the number of immigrants, the farther apart two populations are physically, the less this cohesive force is felt. If two populations become completely isolated, selection will tend to direct evolution in different directions, but as soon as contact is established, gene flow will again tend to unify the two populations.

Random Phenomena

So far we have assumed that the population we are dealing with is a very large one (theoretically infinitely large) and that mating is strictly random. Neither of these two situations is ever met in nature. All populations are finite, and most are medium-sized and go through periods when their numbers are much decreased, particularly in times of hardship (lack of food, extreme temperatures, droughts, and so on). Likewise mating is not random; such simple factors as physical proximity in plant populations and mate preferences among animals, as well as more complicated genetic phenomena such as incompatibility alleles, translocation semisteriles, single matings (such as in bee colonies), make random mating impossible.

The effect of a reduction in size of the population, and of non-randomness of mating, is to make each generation to a certain extent a random sample of the previous one. Consequently the laws of probability become operative. This means that genes may be eliminated or maintained in a population by chance alone. The probability of a gene staying or being eliminated in a population is determined by its frequency, which is the result of mutation, selection, and gene flow. Random fluctuations can occur in populations from year to year that are not the result of selection. These will seldom have long-lasting evolutionary effects, but they will keep the population from reaching its theoretical selective peak. Random phenomena can be of evolutionary significance only when a certain number of important gene arrangements are completely eliminated from the population. The probability of this occurring, even in populations as small as 100 individuals, is very low. It is doubtful that random genetic drift, as this phenomenon is called, has ever been a major positive evolutionary force.

Random phenomena do play a role in other ways. Genes that are in a very low frequency in a population will not likely be present in a random sample, and random phenomena consequently enforce selection. This is also the reason why we said before that unique mutations are not likely to have any effect on the population. Random phenomena also play a role in the establishment of new populations, the so-called Mayr's founder principle: the individuals that establish a new population determine the initial frequency of each gene. However, unless the new population becomes isolated from the rest of the species, in time, gene flow will tend to bring these initial frequencies into balance with those of neighboring populations.

Conclusion

Population genetics is the branch of biology that deals with hereditary phenomena in whole groups of organisms. It is not directly concerned with the mechanism of inheritance but with its effects on the population. Studied is the influence that mutation, recombination, and selection exert on heredity, as well as the effect of the size of the population, the type of mating, the longevity of individuals, and so on. Also considered are the effects that phenomena such as linkage, multiple alleles, sex-linked genes, and many other genetic processes (some of which will be considered in coming chapters) have on the genetic composition of the population. Since all these phenomena can bring about changes in the population, the study of population genetics is thus inevitably related to that of organic evolution.

In this chapter the simplest situation in a population was briefly analyzed: that of two autosomal genes. Such a situation is probably never obtained in nature. Organisms usually differ by several genes. Furthermore seldom does only one gene affect fitness independent of the other genes of the organism. In order to understand the more complex situation found in nature, the simpler one has to be understood first. It is therefore justifiable and of value to study what is rather an abstract laboratory situation.

The population geneticist studies gene frequencies in populations and the phenomena that cause these frequencies to change. His tools are statistics and mathematics as well as experimentation with artificial and natural populations. In the last years, a new tool, computer simulation, has been added. On the basis of theoretical and experimental studies, the population geneticist sets up models to explain general evolutionary phenomena. He then feeds his data into a digital computer, which can predict, on the basis of the given model, what will happen after a set number of generations.

Population genetics is a fascinating study, and one that is full of promise. The student interested in evolution is well advised to become acquainted with this field.

Suggested Further Reading

Dobzhansky, T. *Genetics and the Origin of Species,* 3rd ed. New York: Columbia University Press, 1951, 364 pp. (in particular Chapters 2–4).

Falconer, D. S. *Introduction to Quantitative Genetics.* New York: Ronald Press, 1960, 365 pp. (particularly Chapters 1–6).

Fisher, R. A. *The Genetic Theory of Natural Selection.* New York: Dover Publications, 1958, 291 pp.

Grant, V. *The Origin of Adaptations.* New York: Columbia University Press, 1963, 606 pp. (particularly Chapters 7–11).

Li, C. C. *Population Genetics.* Chicago: University of Chicago Press, 1955, 366 pp. (particularly Chapters 1, 18–20).

Mather, K. *Biometrical Genetics.* New York: Dover Publications, 1949, 155 pp.

Genes and Chromosomes

CHROMOSOMAL CYTOLOGY has played an important role in the modern integrated view of evolution, the synthetic theory of evolution. The importance of chromosomes is twofold: their behavior and characteristics can be used in the classification of species, and secondly, chromosomes can give an insight into genetic phenomena and the evolutionary processes that have brought them about. We will review in this chapter the chromosomal characters that are particularly important in this connection, and some examples in which cytology has been especially helpful as a tool to solve evolutionary problems.

Like all characteristics of an organism, chromosomes and the mechanisms of cell division and of gametic formation are subject to natural selection. Therefore they will vary from species to species, as a result of different evolutionary histories. This variation as a rule is small in related forms, but can be quite large between distantly related groups. Consequently, the study of cytological differences provides good clues as to the probable evolution of a species. But since chromosomes are the carriers of the genetic information, they in turn also influence the evolutionary potential of a species.

Chromosomal Characters

Chromosomes are discrete bodies found in the nucleus of every cell with the possible exception of the blue-green algae (this group of primitive plantlike organisms presumably has not evolved chromosomes yet). Chromosomes are elongate in shape, with a constriction called the centromere somewhere along their length. The centromere divides the chromosomes into two parts, called chromosomal arms. These are of equal length when the centromere is located in the center of the chromosome, or of unequal lengths when the centromere is nearer to one end of the chromosome than the other. If the chromosomal arms are of the same length, we classify the chromosome as having a median centromere; if not exactly in the middle, we speak of a submedian centromere; if near one end, we call it a subterminal centromere; and if almost at the end (apparently it is never on the very end), it is designated as a terminal centromere. The position of the centromere, then, provides a basis for the classification and identification of chromosomes.

A second way to identify chromosomes is by their length. The length of the chromosomes varies from about 1 micron to 30 microns, with most chromosomes being less than 10 microns in length during the stage of maximum contraction in mitosis. Absolute length and relative length of the two chromosomal arms are the main, and often the only, ways to recognize individual chromosomes in a cell.

Sometimes chromosomes can be identified by additional characteristics. A very frequent one is the possession at one end of a small, usually rounded body called a satellite, which is united to the main body of the chromosome by a thin, threadlike filament called a secondary constriction. Usually only one pair of homologous chromosomes possesses a satellite. An individual chromosome does not have more than one satellite. Another characteristic by which chromosomes can sometimes be distinguished is the presence of distinct areas of strongly staining material called heterochromatin. These areas can be best observed during mitotic prophase, but since this stage usually is comparatively difficult to study, heterochromatic areas are not commonly very useful in identifying chromosomes.

Each chromosome has a morphologically similar partner in a regular body cell (excluding the gametes). One member of the pair was contributed by the sperm, or male gamete, the other by the egg, or female gamete. But in one sex of most animals and some plants, a pair is found in which the mates are not similar: these are the sex chromosomes. The male (in the XY system common to most mammals and insects) or the female (in the ZW system found in most birds, fishes, and some insects) has one chromosome of each type; the other sex has two of the same type (either two X's or two W's).

Chromosome Number

The number of chromosomes in the nucleus of the cells of the individuals of a species is constant and characteristic for that species.

All the cells of an organism are derived from the product of the fusion of two gametes. This first cell is called a zygote. In each division of the zygote and its products, the chromosomes split longitudinally, and consequently all the cells of an organism have the same number and type of chromosomes. In certain tissues longitudinal division of the chromosomes takes place without the corresponding division of the cell. This produces cells with twice or

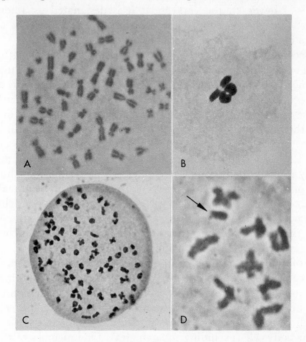

Figure 4·1. A: Somatic chromosomes in man $(2n = 46)$. **B:** Metaphase I division in *Haplopappus gracilis* $(n = 2)$; this is the lowest chromosome number so far known in a plant [photo courtesy Dr. Ray Jackson]. **C:** Diakinesis in the fern *Polystichum californicum* $(n = 82)$; ferns are often characterized by very high numbers of chromosomes [photo courtesy Dr. Warren H. Wagner]. **D:** Diakinesis in *Gutierrezia bracteata* $(n = 8 + 1)$; arrow points to supernumerary chromosome.

even four times the number of chromosomes present in the zygote. In this process, called endomitosis, the number but not the morphology of the chromosomes is changed. Endomitosis is of physiological but not of genetic importance, since it does not occur regularly in the cells of tissues that lead to the formation of gametes. The number of chromosomes in somatic cells varies from a minimum of two pairs—found in one plant, *Haplopappus gracilis* of the sunflower family (Figure 4·1) and in several insects and lower animals—to several hundred. The majority of species of plants and animals have between 5 and 30 pairs of chromosomes. Man has 23 pairs (Figure 4·1). One animal, *Ascaris megalocephala* var. *univalens,* has one chromosome in meiosis and in the germinative line, but the chromosome, fragments into several in the somatic line.

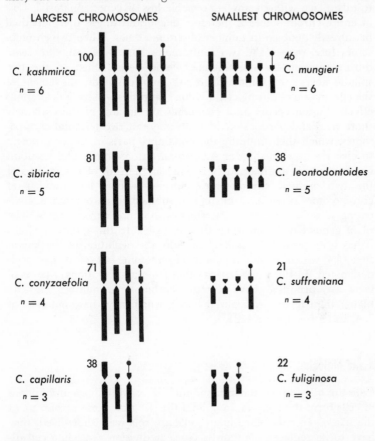

LARGEST CHROMOSOMES   SMALLEST CHROMOSOMES

C. kashmirica   100   46 *C. mungieri*
n = 6   n = 6

C. sibirica   81   38 *C. leontodontoides*
n = 5   n = 5

C. conyzaefolia 71   21 *C. suffreniana*
n = 4   n = 4

C. capillaris   38   22 *C. fuliginosa*
n = 3   n = 3

Figure 4·2. Evolution of the chromosomes in two lines of Crepis. The most primitive species in each line are at the top of the figure, the most advanced at the bottom. Numbers refer to the relative length of the chromosomes, considering *Crepis kashmirica* as 100. [From E. B. Babcock, *The Genus Crepis*, Part I. Berkeley: University of California Press, 1947. Botany series, Vol. 21.]

Although the number of chromosomes is constant, occasionally changes do occur in the gametes or in tissues that lead to the formation of gametes. These can occur in two main ways: by division of the chromosomes in a cell that is going to give rise to the gametes without the division of the cell itself, yielding a cell with exactly double the original number of chromosomes; or by fusion or breakage of individual chromosomes. The latter way gives rise to cells with one or two chromosomes in excess or in deficiency. To be viable, increases and decreases in the number of chromosomes have to take place without any appreciable loss of genetic material. Loss of entire chromosomes is therefore deleterious unless the individual has already doubled its number of chromosomes. When two chromosomes fuse, one of the two centromeres has to be lost. Otherwise during division the chromosome would be attached to the two spindle fibers (the spindle fibers are involved in the movement of the chromosomes during cell division), and this will have deleterious effects. Fusion occurs most commonly by the loss of the extremely short arms and portions of the centromere of two terminal chromosomes, which then unite by the remaining parts of the centromere to give rise to a median or submedian chromosome. The resultant chromosome is approximately as long as the sum of the lengths of the two original chromosomes. Species with a low number of chromosomes often have median or submedian chromosomes, indicating a reduction from ancestors with more chromosomes. The plant genus *Crepis* illustrates this very well. In this group of plants it has been possible to follow carefully the evolution of the karyotype, by which name the basic chromosome set of a species is designated. In this genus, species that from an evolutionary point of view are primitive have a basic chromosome number $(n = 6)$ higher than related specialized forms, which have base numbers of 5, 4, and 3 (see Figure $4 \cdot 2$).

Mitosis and Meiosis

Cells are all of about the same minute size, and millions and billions of cells form the body of an animal the size of a horse or of a plant the size of an oak. Since many cells are relatively short-lived, they have to be replaced constantly. Nuclear division preceding cell division is a complex process known as mitosis. It will be assumed that the reader is familiar with the general outline and details of this process.

Cell division in a number of ways varies widely from species to species, and there are also some striking differences of detail between plants and animals. The essential process of mitosis is nevertheless basically similar in all organisms. During division of the nucleus a mechanism has to be provided for an exact distribution to the daughter cells of the particles of heredity, the genes. Although

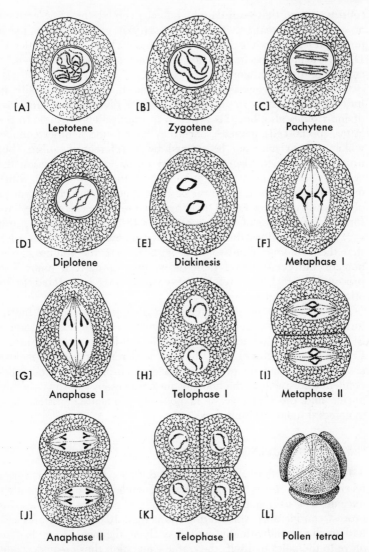

Figure 4·3. Meiosis. Schematic representation of the different stages of meiosis in a hypothetical plant with two pairs of chromosomes.

mitotic peculiarities can sometimes be used to identify groups of animals or plants, such as in species with diffuse centromeres, these instances are rare.

From a genetic point of view, the most important feature of mitosis is the exact copying of the chromosome and of the main constituents, so that both daughter nuclei receive the same amount of genetic information. This is necessary if genetic continuity is to be preserved in the species. The physicochemical properties of DNA provide a mechanism for the exact copying of the genetic content of the chromosomes.

Cell division provides for growth and maintenance of life in individual organisms. In unicellular ones, cell division means increase of individuals also, but this is not so in multicellular beings. In the latter, special cells, gametes, once they have found another gamete, which may or may not be formed by a different organism (but usually is), fuse to form a zygote. By mitosis and cell division the zygote gives rise to a new individual of the same species. Since during fertilization—the fusion of two gametes—the chromosomes of the two cells are added together, before the next gametes are formed the number of chromosomes has to be halved. If not, in a very few generations the number of chromosomes would be such that their volume alone would be greater than the volume of the nucleus and even greater than the volume of the cell itself. The process by which the number of chromosomes is restored to its original value is known as meiosis.

Meiosis consists of two consecutive divisions and results in the formation of four daughter nuclei (Figure 4·3). Nuclear division is followed or accompanied by cytoplasmic division in most organisms. From a genetic point of view, the most important features of meiosis are the exact halving of the number of chromosomes, the independent assortment of the homologous chromosomes to the daughter nuclei, and the exchange of homologous segments of sister chromosomes through crossing-over.

LINKAGE AND CROSSING-OVER

It is essential that in each nuclear division, the daughter nuclei receive exact copies of the genetic complement of the mother nucleus. The aggregation of genes into chromosomes simplifies this process considerably, since if the more than 10,000 genes in a cell had to divide individually, and if each of the two halves had to move to the poles by itself, the traffic congestion thus created would undoubtedly result in unequal daughter nuclei. It is unlikely that under such circumstances complex multicellular organisms could have evolved. The blue-green algae, which are very simple organisms, have no chromosomes, and this might account in part for their great structural simplicity. The stringing of the genes into chromosomes has made equal divisions of the chromosomes possible, but also has had the effect of limiting the independent assortment of genes. In effect, at meiosis, all the genes in a chromosome have to move together to the same pole. This phenomenon is known as linkage, and it is of considerable genetic importance.

Genes in different chromosomes are not linked, while those in the same chromosome are. Given a certain number of genes for a particular species, it follows that the groups of mutually linked genes will be of the same number as chromosomes of that species. The lower the number of linkage groups with a constant number of genes, the higher the number of genes in each linkage group, and the less operative the law of independent assortment. The phenomenon was first observed by two British geneticists, W. Bateson and R. C. Punnett, in 1906. When they crossed plants of sweet peas that were purple-flowered and had elongated ("long") pollen grains, with plants that were red-flowered and had round pollen grains, they obtained plants that were all purple-flowered with elongated pollen grains, indicating that purple flowers and elongated pollen grains were dominant. In the F_2, they obtained the four combinations expected according to independent assortment of the genes (purple/long, purple/round, red/long, red/round), not in the $9:3:3:1$ ratio expected. Instead the two parental combinations, purple/long and red/round, were present in excess over expectations. The proportion of the four classes was approximately $11:1:1:3$. This was a surprising result at the time.

The answer to this riddle had to await work on the fruit fly *Drosophila* (1910–1915) by the American Thomas H. Morgan. Bateson and Punnett had shown that the law of independent assortment did not apply in this case, but if linkage was complete, only the parental types should be present. The presence of purple-flowered peas with round pollen and of red-flowered plants with elongated pollen, as Morgan showed, is due to the exchange of corresponding segments of two chromatids belonging to homologous chromosomes during meiosis. This phenomenon is called crossing-over (Figure 4·4). The number of cross-overs occurring in a chromosome depends on several factors, such as the genetic constitution of the species and the individual, and the length of the chromosome. Cross-overs occur along the length of a chromosome (within certain limits), apparently at random. The chances that one will occur between two given genes in a chromosome depends on the distance separating the genes and the frequency with which cross-overs occur in a chromosome. Thus linkage depends on the number of chromosomes, the frequency of cross-overs in each chromosome, and the size of the chromosomes.

Linkage is a phenomenon that controls the rate at which non-allelic genes on the same chromosome will mix with other such genes in homologous chromosomes coming from different parents. If linkage is absolute, only the parental types will be produced, and no new combinations will be present. If, on the other hand, there is no linkage, there will be random assortment, and the chances of the parental combinations surviving will be very low. In situations where parental combinations are very successful, natural selection

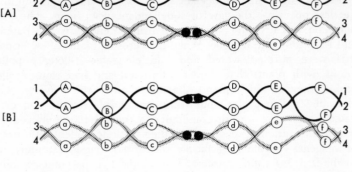
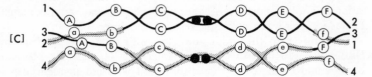
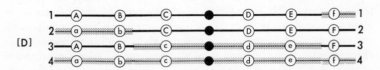

Figure 4·4. Sketch to show recombination as a result of crossing-over. Single cross-overs take place at **B** between chromatids 1 and 3 and 2 and 3, that result in three recombinant and one nonrecombinant chromosome after meiosis as shown in **D**.

will favor mechanisms that increase linkage. On the other hand, when a variable offspring is advantageous, natural selection will favor less linkage and an increase in the number of recombinant types. Some of the mechanisms that increase linkage are a lowering of the rate of crossing-over, a lower number of chromosomes, and the rearrangement of beneficial genes in close physical proximity on the same chromosome. This last is the result of transverse breakages and reunions of the broken ends of one or more chromosomes in novel ways. How these particular changes come about we do not exactly know. But when they take place, they will be favored (and maintained) by natural selection in the populations where less linkage is advantageous, and they will be eliminated in those populations where less linkage is not desirable.

If the species is found in an environment that does not change or changes very little, there will be little selective pressure favoring the production of many recombinants. On the other hand, if the species lives in a constantly changing environment, producing very many different types of recombinants so that some will be able to cope with the changes will probably be favored by natural selection. Other factors also play a role. For example, an organism that has numerous offspring can afford to lose more than one that produces few descendants.

Natural selection therefore operates to control the amount of linkage and recombination. In every situation the individuals in a population with the best "compromise" between linkage and recombination will be able to produce the more numerous surviving offspring.

Haploid, Diploid, and Polyploid

The zygote, the first cell of the organism, which is the product of the fusion of two gametes, has two sets of chromosomes. Each is furnished by one of the parents, and consequently the zygote is diploid. But not all organisms are diploid. In some cases, particularly among plants, the spores produced at meiosis form an organism without previous fusion. Such organisms have only one set of chromosomes and are haploid. Finally, due to accidents of development, the gametes, the zygote, or a cell produced by the zygote may double its number of chromosomes. The resulting organisms will have more than two sets of chromosomes and will be called triploid, tetraploid, pentaploid, hexaploid, and so on, according to the number of sets of chromosomes present; they are also referred to as polyploids.

Polyploidy is rare among animals, but is very frequent in plants, where it has played an important evolutionary role. A plant with exactly twice the number of chromosomes of its progenitors is qualitatively like them, since no new genetic information has been added. But the additional sets of chromosomes usually have the effect of increasing the size of the cells, and at the same time of decreasing the total number of cells. In a tetraploid the first effect outweighs the second, and the plants are usually larger (which is of immediate application in horticulture). With further doubling of the chromosomes, the net effect is often a decrease in size of the plants.

Polyploids are often sterile. Since now there are four homologous chromosomes, at meiosis they tend to pair together, and instead of bivalents, tetravalents are formed. These do not necessarily separate to the poles two by two, and the result is the formation of gametes that lack some chromosomes and have an excess of others. (Figure 4·1).

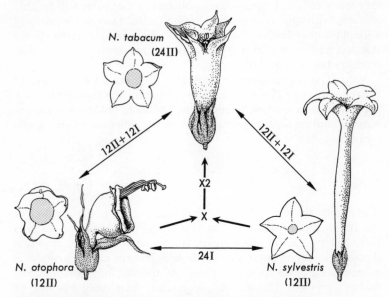

Figure 4·5. Probable origin of the tobacco plant, *Nicotiana tabacum*, as a result of hybridization followed by chromosome doubling between *N. otophora* and *N. sylvestris*. [Data from Goodspeed, "The Genus Nicotiana," Waltham, Mass.: Chronica Botanica Co., 1954.]

There is nevertheless a special kind of polyploid that is fertile. If two distantly related species cross, their chromosomes may not pair at all. Instead univalents are formed at meiosis, and consequently the hybrid plant will be sterile. If in such a plant the chromosomes are doubled, fertility is restored, since now there will be two of each type of chromosome. Such a hybrid is an allopolyploid, to distinguish it from the former type, which is an autopolyploid. An example of an allopolyploid is the tobacco plant *Nicotiana tabacum*. Tobacco is the result of the doubling of the chromosomes of the natural hybrid between *Nicotiana otophora* and *N. sylvestris.* This cross occurred naturally some hundreds or maybe thousands of years ago, but it has been successfully repeated under artificial conditions (Figure 4·5).

A third type of polyploid is an intermediate between the two just listed: some of the chromosomes of the two parents are sufficiently related so that they will pair, others are not. This is a

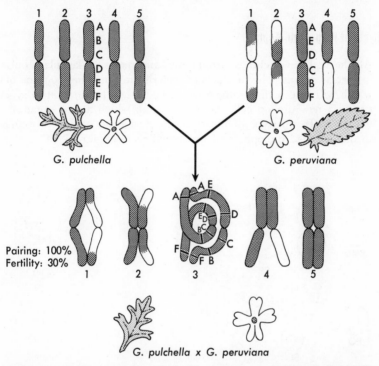

Pairing: 100%
Fertility: 30%

G. pulchella

G. peruviana

G. pulchella x *G. peruviana*

Figure 4·6. Pairing and fertility relationships between two species of *Glandularia* (Verbenaceae). Although the chromosomes of the hybrid paired, fertility was very low because of large segments that were nonhomologous (indicated by shading in the illustration). When the number of chromosomes in the hybrid was doubled, fertility was increased, since every chromosome now had an exact homologous to pair with at meiosis. [Data from Schnack and Solbrig, 1953.]

segmental allopolyploid. Its fate depends largely on whether the allo or the auto components prevail (Figure 4·6). Most natural polyploids are either allopolyploids or segmental allopolyploids. A few natural autopolyploids are also known.

Polyploidy is the only important mechanism known by which new species can be formed suddenly and without isolation. In effect, when a tetraploid is crossed with one of its parental diploids, the offspring is triploid. Two of each group of homologous chromosomes are from one parent and one from the other. At meiosis two chromosomes will go to one pole and one to the other randomly for each group of three homologues. The gametes will have odd numbers of chromosomes and will be sterile. The tetraploid is consequently reproductively isolated from its diploid ancestors.

Life Cycle of Plants and Animals

All the higher vertebrates are diploid, and meiosis takes place only in special organs. The products of meiosis are the gametes, some of which will fuse with a gamete produced by another animal to give rise to a new diploid cell, the zygote, from which a new organism will arise. In this type of life cycle the developed organism occurs in the so-called diplophase of the sexual cycle (Figure 4·7).

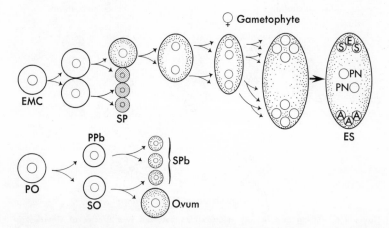

Figure 4·7. Female gametogenesis in flowering plants (*above*) **and mammals** (*below*). Note that in mammals the egg is the only functional cell; in plants a series of haploid cells—the female gametophyte—is functional. EMC = embryo sac mother cell; SP = spores; E = egg; S = synergids; PN = polar nuclei; A = antipodals; PO = primary oocyte; SO = secondary oocyte; PPb = primary polar body; SPb = secondary polar body.

But this is not the case with all organisms. In many, the products of meiosis do not become gametes, but divide mitotically to form an independent organism. That is the case of the mosses, where the diplophase alternates with the so-called haplophase which results from the division of the products of meiosis (Figure 4·8). An alternation of generations is universal in all the land plants (and

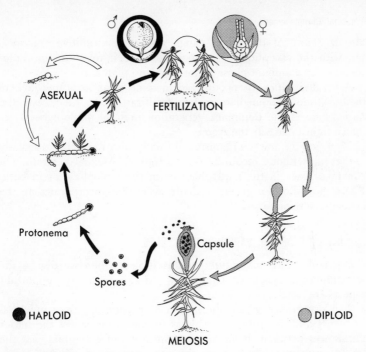

ASEXUAL

FERTILIZATION

Protonema

Capsule

Spores

● HAPLOID   ○ DIPLOID

MEIOSIS

Figure 4·8. Life cycle of a moss. Note that the moss plant is haploid; only the capsule is diploid.

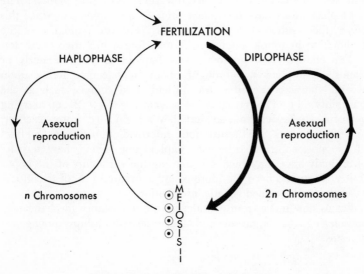

FERTILIZATION

HAPLOPHASE   DIPLOPHASE

Asexual reproduction

Asexual reproduction

n Chromosomes   2n Chromosomes

MEIOSIS

Figure 4·9. Generalized life-cycle diagram.

also in many of the algae, fungi, and some primitive animals), but with the exception of the mosses and their relatives, the diplophase is the dominant phase among the land plants.

A third situation is encountered in some algae and fungi, where meiosis follows immediately after fertilization. In such cases the haplophase is the dominant generation and the diplophase is reduced to just one cell, the zygote.

Many of the lower organisms normally also reproduce asexually —that is, without recourse to fertilization. Asexual reproduction can take place in the haplophase or in the diplophase or in both. Figure 4·9 shows a generalized life cycle that incorporates all the elements here discussed.

SIGNIFICANCE OF THE VARIOUS LIFE CYCLES

We will return more fully to this subject when we discuss the recombination system in Chapter 6. At this point two important aspects are worth pointing out.

The occurrence of an alternation of generations is so universal in plants and so rare in animals as to constitute one of the major differences between them. More significant still is the fact that the lower organisms usually have either an alternation of generations or the occurrence of the developed organism in the haplophase. In the more developed organisms the haplophase is restricted to the gametes (animals) or to a very few cells (flowering plants). The haplophase must have developed prior to the diplophase, since this last is the result of fusion of two cells. The predominance of the haplophase in simple organisms is therefore a primitive character.

The change from predominantly haploid to predominantly or exclusively diploid was brought about by selection acting upon several characteristics that the diploid state confers, such as the possibility (1) of carrying twice as many genes; (2) of carrying genes in a recessive state so that they are shielded from selection; and (3) of novel genetic situations, intermediate between the effect of the genes contributed by each haploid line. These characteristics of diploidy have the effect of increasing the variability of the population. They also permit a more complex organism in all likelihood, as a result of the added genetic information.

Let us now move from considering the inheritance mechanism to considering the organism and the interrelationships among organisms.

Suggested Further Reading

Bateson, W., and R. C. Punnett. "Experimental Studies in the Physiology of Heredity." Reports to the Evolution Committee of the Royal Society (London), Reps. 2, 3, and 4, 1905–08. Reproduced in J. A. Peters, *Classical Papers in Genetics.* Englewood Cliffs, N.J.: Prentice-Hall, 1961, pp. 42–59.

Lewis, H. "Genetics and Cytology in Relation to Taxonomy." *Taxon, 6:*42–46, 1957.

Stebbins, G. L. "Types of Polyploids: Their Classification and Significance." *Adv. in Genetics, 1:*403–430, 1947.

———— "The Comparative Evolution of Genetic Systems." In S. Tax (ed.), *Evolution After Darwin,* Vol. 1. Chicago: University of Chicago Press, 1960.

Swanson, C. P. *Cytology and Cytogenetics.* Englewood Cliffs, N.J.: Prentice-Hall, 1957.

Wetmore, R. H., A. E. De Maggio, and G. Morel. "A Morphogenetic Look at the Alternation of Generations." *J. Indian Bot. Soc., 42A:*306–320, 1964.

White, M. J. D. *Animal Cytology and Evolution.* New York: Oxford University Press, 1952.

5

Individuals, Populations, and Species

NEARLY EVERY PART of the earth's surface is inhabited by living organisms, from the tropics to the polar latitudes, and from the great ocean depths to high in the atmosphere. Their multitude is enormous; their forms, shapes, and ways of life are so varied that no limit is apparent. All this multiplicity is but an expression of an advanced level of chemical organization that we call life. Nucleic acids, proteins, lipids, water, a certain number of minerals, and carbohydrate fuel, organized into little vesicles with semipermeable membranes, are common to all organisms, from the tiny blue-green algae and bacteria to the giant whales.

Evolutionary Units

Wherever we look, be it up into the skies, or down into the oceans, deep into matter or away out into the universe, we find a multiplicity of level upon level of systems of organization, all interrelated and all of them fantastically complex. When we observe and study this variety of forms we instinctively think of the level of organization to which we as individuals belong, the level of the individual organism, as the unit of measure. Any system below that of the individual is thought of as "small" or "simple," anything above it as "large" and "complex." But the individual organism is a level of organization that is sometimes hard to define. The notion that an individual is not divisible without losing its properties of "life" is applicable to most higher animals. But most plants and many of the so-called lower animals can be broken up into smaller units, each of which is capable of regenerating the missing segments, a fact of which we take advantage when we obtain new plants through cuttings.

Furthermore in some cases "individuals" cannot live by themselves but need to aggregate with other individuals. The lichens are the most striking example. These plants are formed by an alga and a fungus that live in close association. The algae that occur in lichens usually also occur alone, but nearly all of the lichen fungi are restricted to their lichen occurrence. No other examples are as striking as the lichens, but a long list of parasites and symbionts are directly dependent on other individuals for their life, although such a relationship is not always mutual. Man, for example, depends not only on plants and animals for food, but also on the colon bacterium, *Escherichia coli,* which manufactures vitamin K, without which we could not live. *Escherichia coli,* in turn, cannot live under natural conditions outside of the colon.

Another type of organization is represented by colonial forms. Such diverse organisms as the green algae *Volvox* and *Pandorina,* honeybees and ants, exist in close association, where each member performs roles that are vital to all the others. In these colonial forms individual members can no longer survive alone. The unit is the colony and not the individual member. But then, with the exception of hermaphroditic, self-fertile plants and of a few parthenogenetic plants and animals, all organisms are incomplete, since they cannot reproduce by themselves. The minimum needed is two individuals of opposite sex. Furthermore organisms do not occur in isolated pairs, but in groups of variable numbers of different sexes and ages at each locality. These groups are known as breeding populations. A population is spatially confined, and a reality only in sexually reproducing species.

A further type of organization is the community. The population is a genetic unit, held together in time by reproduction and descent. The community is an ecological unit. It is formed by one or more breeding populations of the same or different species that are adapted to the same environment. Communities include plants and animals, both microscopic and multicellular. To the extent that every organism modifies the environment in which it lives, it is a factor in the environment, and consequently there is a certain interrelationship between the members of the community. This relationship is a very loose one, as are the physical limits of the community. But communities are ecological units that conform to certain criteria and have a certain continuity in time, and as such have an undeniable existence.

One of the major characteristics of matter, including living matter, is that it is organized. Individuals, symbionts, colonial forms, breeding populations, are not the products of chance, but represent a highly integrated system of organization. But at the same time it is not always easy to define all of these levels. The reasons for this are many and different for each particular instance. But this much can be generalized: no two situations in evolution are alike. The quality and rate of mutation, the recombination system, the ecological situation to which organisms have to adapt, are unique in each population, in each colony, in each community. The Douglas fir grows continuously over thousands of acres in North America, and no discrete breeding populations can be discovered; on the other hand, the swamp maple is restricted to wet areas where it forms dense stands; rabbits are found throughout the Prairie and Great Basin forming loose pairs, while prairie dogs which also live in that area form colonies of hundreds of individuals.

We have already seen that the breeding population is a basic evolutionary unit. But the major evolutionary unit is not the population but the species.

The Concept of the Species

Classes of organisms called species have been recognized for a long time, but there has been and still is much confusion as to what a species really is.

There are three main species concepts. The first is that of the philosopher and the logician. Theirs is a concept that goes back all the way to Aristotle. Species is a category of thought, more specifically a logical class to which belong all the objects (be they living or not) that have certain common properties. So, for example, fork is a species, all forks having certain basic common properties, such as the possession of prongs or tines and a handle arranged in such a way that objects can be both lifted and pierced. Within these limitations, forks can be of different shapes, sizes, and materials.

The second criterion, the so-called morphological criterion of biologists, is an application of the logical definition of species to organisms. Species are defined strictly on the possession by their members of certain morphological characteristics not possessed by members of other species. This was the concept of species held by Linnaeus and most eighteenth- and nineteenth-century taxonomists, and even in our day it is adhered to strictly by some.

Finally the third criterion is the so-called "biological species concept." The individuals of populations that under natural conditions are potentially capable of interbreeding form the species. The morphological species concept stresses likeness and similarity, while the biological species concept stresses the breeding relationships. In general there is a high degree of coincidence between the species defined by these two concepts. Individuals that look alike tend to interbreed; and individuals that interbreed tend to look alike, since they have large numbers of common genes. There are nevertheless cases when this is not so. Sexual dimorphism is a striking case, such as in the case of the mallard duck, where Linnaeus applying a strict morphological criterion described the male and female as different species. Other cases of dimorphism are not tied to sex. Many species of flowering plants have individuals with different flower colors, such as the small genus *Leavenworthia* of the mustard family, where some species have individuals with white flowers and individuals with yellow flowers; or white and pink wild radishes all belonging to the same breeding population. Snails of the species *Cepaea nemoralis* have different banding patterns in the shell, and so forth.

The species can be considered the largest populational unit. Individuals in a population usually mate with individuals of the same population. Occasionally an animal will wander away from its breeding population, or a seed from a plant will be blown away by the wind. In such instances individuals from different populations will exchange genes, but with members of their same species (with some exceptions). There are definite barriers to the exchange of genes between different species, which can be spatial, temporal, ecological, behavioral, cytological, or genetical.

Higher Categories

Species are grouped into larger categories called genera, which in turn are grouped into families, orders, classes, phyla, and kingdoms (see Table 5·1). While the categories discussed so far—individuals, breeding populations, communities, and species—are natural, nonarbitrary categories, the higher ones are ideal, logical categories (Figure 5·1). They are classes to which all the categories of the next lower level having certain characters in common belong. So, for example, the genus *Felis* is formed by all the species of mammals with claws and certain types of dentition, such as cats, lions, tigers. But although the genus *Felis* is a useful concept that helps us to express in one word a certain relationship, and although probably all the species of *Felis* have had a common origin, there is no tangible reality to the genus *Felis,* as there is to the species *Felis leo,* the lion. The different species of the genus

TABLE 5·1

The Major Categories Used in Classification

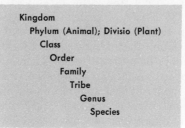

Kingdom
   Phylum (Animal); Divisio (Plant)
      Class
         Order
            Family
               Tribe
                  Genus
                     Species

Intermediate categories can be erected using the prefixes *sub* and (in animal taxonomy) *super*, such as subclass, superfamily, and the like.

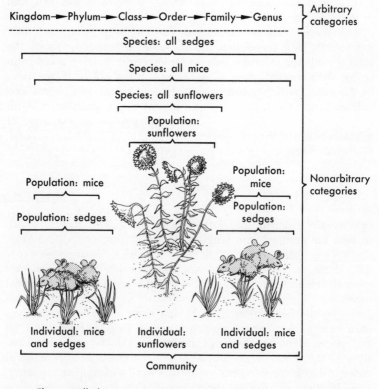

Kingdom→Phylum→Class→Order→Family→Genus } Arbitrary categories

Species: all sedges

Species: all mice

Species: all sunflowers

Population: sunflowers

Population: mice

Population: sedges

Population: mice

Population: sedges

Nonarbitrary categories

Individual: mice and sedges

Individual: sunflowers

Individual: mice and sedges

Community

Flora = All plants   Fauna = All animals

Figure 5·1. Sketch showing relationships between different categories.

usually cannot breed with each other, they are not subjected to
the same selection pressures, they do not live in the same environment, and although they may have had a common origin, they
do not have a common present or future.

A hierarchical system of categories in which the groups on each
level are formed by placing together those of the level below has
become a fundamental aspect of the taxonomic method. It was
essentially established by Linnaeus in the eighteenth century and
still persists today. This system has provided a means to reveal
relationships, but it also has often proved inadequate as a way of
expressing certain conclusions about the interrelationships of organisms. This has led some scientists, especially cytologists, geneticists,
and ecologists, to reject the classical system and to construct their
own system of categories. On the other hand, it also has resulted
in disregarding or minimizing genetic and breeding information in
systematic studies by some of the more orthodox taxonomists. Although the rigidity of the hierarchical system occasionally proves
inadequate in expressing certain relationships, it has proven the
best system so far devised. We will come back to this point in
Chapter 9 when discussing the operations involved in classification.

Models of Speciation

One of the problems that has concerned biologists most has been
the origin of species. Darwin chose to entitle his famous book with
these words (although he did not solve the problem), and it has
been the subject of many scholarly discussions and some heated
arguments ever since. The reasons for so much interest in this
subject is that the formation of new species is one of the crucial
aspects of evolution.

Table 5·2 indicates some of the major known models explaining
the ways species can arise. Phyletic speciation is transformation in
time due to mutation, recombination, and selection. Hybridization
and fusion with other species to various degrees provide other means
of transformation of species in time. But true speciation is not
change but multiplication of species. If we recall our definition of
species—"a reproductively isolated population or group of populations"—the problem of the multiplication of species is to explain
how reproductive isolation arises between groups of populations.

New species can originate when a single individual or a very
few individuals become reproductively isolated from the remainder
of the population in which they are growing, or new species can
originate when a whole population becomes isolated from the rest

of the populations of the mother species. The first is apparently the rarer of the two situations and is largely to be found in the plant kingdom.

TABLE 5·2

Potential Modes of Origin of Species

I. Transformation of species (*Phyletic speciation*)
   1. Autogenous transformation (owing to mutation, selection, etc.)
   2. Allogenous transformation (owing to introgression from other species)

II. Multiplication of species (*true speciation*)
   1. Instantaneous speciation (through individuals)
      (a) Chromosomal rearrangements
      (b) Polyploidy
   2. Gradual speciation (through populations)
      (a) Sympatric speciation
      (b) Allopatric speciation (*geographic speciation*)

Source: Adapted from Mayr, *Animal Species and Evolution.* Cambridge: Belknap Press of Harvard University Press, 1963.

A single individual can acquire reproductive isolation and give rise to a new species by mutations that suddenly isolate it from the other plants or animals with which it grows without affecting its own fertility. Genes are known in certain species that produce breaks in the chromosomes and lead to rearrangements of the linear order of the genes in the chromosomes. Individuals with a new arrangement can cross with individuals having the ancestral type, but the offspring to a large extent is sterile, because the chromosomes fail to pair at meiosis. This is not the case with the offspring resulting from the cross of two organisms having the same type of chromosomal arrangement. Nevertheless the probabilities that two animals would acquire the same mutation simultaneously or nearly so and the chance that the same chromosomal rearrangements will be produced are practically nil. This model of speciation can therefore be discounted in the animal kingdom, at least for the higher animals. On the other hand, among self-fertile, hermaphroditic plants, a single mutation suffices, and there is the distinct possibility that such has been the origin of at least one species, *Clarkia franciscana* Lewis and Raven, of the evening primrose family. Since the change is in the order of the genes, but apparently not in their quality or quantity, little morphological change is to be expected in a species originating in this manner.

The second type of instantaneous speciation involves doubling the number of chromosomes, which has the same effect as alteration of the structure: organisms usually only produce fertile offspring when crossed with individuals with the same number of chromosomes. Polyploidy is frequent among plants, particularly the flowering plants, where up to 40 per cent of all species might have originated in this manner (for more details see Chapter 4).

But by far the largest number of species have originated by gradual speciation through the isolation of populations, rather than individuals. This model is usually called geographic or allopatric speciation. To understand how geographic speciation works we must first look into the nature of the isolating mechanisms and into the specific role of variation.

INFRASPECIFIC AND INTERSPECIFIC VARIATION

In Chapter 3 we analyzed the dynamics of breeding populations and the forces that tend to produce uniformity and also those forces that disrupt uniformity. These forces—mutation, recombination, and selection—acting independently on different breeding populations, tend to produce slightly different adjustments to the environment. How different these adjustments are will depend on how much the environments differ between different breeding populations, on the amount of gene flow, and to a lesser extent on random phenomena. The result is a tendency for different breeding

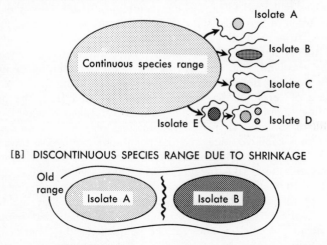

[A] DISCONTINUOUS SPECIES RANGE DUE TO EXPANSION

Isolate A
Isolate B
Continuous species range
Isolate C
Isolate E   Isolate D

[B] DISCONTINUOUS SPECIES RANGE DUE TO SHRINKAGE

Old range
Isolate A   Isolate B

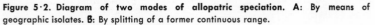

Figure 5·2. Diagram of two modes of allopatric speciation. A: By means of geographic isolates. B: By splitting of a former continuous range.

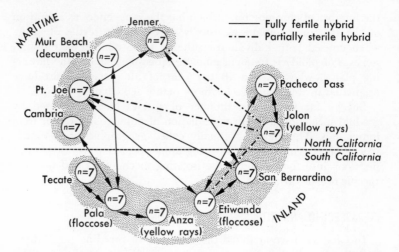

Figure 5·3. Diagram of intraspecific crosses within the species *Layia platiglossa.* Note also how certain populations have acquired novel morphological characters. Nevertheless, there are only incipient sterility barriers. [From J. Clausen, *Stages in the Evolution of Plant Species,* copyright 1951 by Cornell University. Used by permission of Cornell University Press.]

populations of a species to be slightly different genetically, physiologically, and morphologically. The greater the gene flow between two populations, the more closely related they will be, and vice versa.

It follows that populations from opposite extremes of the range of a species will tend to be the most different. In the fringes of the distribution of a species, suitable environments are often scarce and isolated from each other. Where a forest merges with grassland, we will usually have an area of small pockets of woods in the midst of the grassland. The same is true for example at the upper limits of the forest in the mountains. A forest species living in one of the pockets of forest in the prairie becomes isolated from the other breeding populations. Such populations are called geographic or peripheral isolates. In peripheral isolates, gene flow is no longer acting as a cohesive force, and the population can evolve toward a balance with its environment at a faster rate. Since the environment of isolates is marginal to the species, as we have seen, natural selection will tend to modify peripheral populations considerably. In due time some of the many forms of reproductive isolation may build up between the isolate and the original species. When that happens the isolate becomes a new species adapted to the intermediate habitat, in this case the pockets of woodland in midst of the grassland (Figure 5·2).

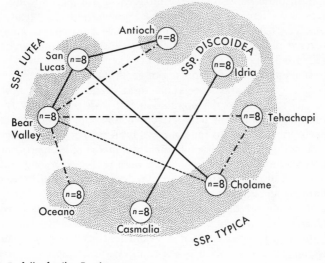

—————— F_1 fully fertile, F_2 vigorous
-------- F_1 fully fertile, F_2 reduced in vigor
··—·— F_1 partially sterile, F_2 reduced in vigor

Figure 5·4. Crossing relationships between populations of *Layia glandulosa*. In contrast to the case of *L. platiglossa*, in this species there are already some sterility barriers between populations. [From J. Clausen, *Stages in the Evolution of Plant Species*, copyright 1951 by Cornell University. Used by permission of Cornell University Press.]

Actually it is fairly rare for peripheral isolates to become new species. The reasons for this are many. Species colonize peripheral situations to which they are not too well adapted in years when the environmental conditions are extremely favorable. When conditions worsen, the invaders usually cannot compete and are eliminated. Furthermore the processes leading to speciation require a series of conditions, such as favorable mutations and/or recombinations, evolution of an isolating mechanism, and conditions that permit survival of the isolated population, a combination of requirements seldom found together.

But speciation can take place also during times of shrinkage of the range of the species. If for reasons of unfavorable environmental conditions the species decreases its range, the continuity of the area occupied may be split into two or more areas. We have already mentioned that within a continuous area, populations at the extremes tend to be quite different, sometimes to the point that some degree of reduced fertility exists when individuals of these populations are bred (see Figure 5·3). Since the gene flow is through the intermediate populations, the integrity of the species is not affected. But if suddenly these intermediate populations disappear, the differences between the extremes become paramount, and if they survive they are often on their way toward becoming new species (Figure 5·4).

In contrast with the concept of geographic or allopatric speciation is that of sympatric speciation—that is, the origin of new species by the splitting of the population into two reproductively isolated breeding populations without spatial isolation. Several models have been proposed but so far none has been proven to be without flaws. The major difficulty is explaining in a model of sympatric speciation how reproductive isolation can be built up between some individuals and not others in an interbreeding population. Furthermore, it is hard to imagine that two groups of organisms very closely related and occupying the same habitat can coexist without competition. Competition will sooner or later wipe out one of the two. The first individual to become isolated would find itself without a mate and would not survive. If it is self-fertile it might represent instantaneous speciation, but even then unless the isolated individual moves away it probably would not be able to stand competition and would be eliminated.

Nevertheless, some intermediate situations exist that are occasionally referred to as sympatric speciation. These involve isolation in time or adaptation to very different ecological situations existing within short distances. The mechanism in these cases always involves first a breaking up of the population into isolated groups by breeding either at different times or in different places, and subsequently a development of isolating barriers that keep the populations from interbreeding if they then come together.

Character Displacement

Only where the cruising ranges of two similar animal species or the areas of effective pollination of two like plant species overlap can there be absolute certainty that two distinct but closely related breeding populations are indeed two species. In such cases there cannot be any doubt: if they have developed breeding isolation they will not mix; if they mix, they have not yet developed breeding isolation.

When two such closely related animal species formed allopatrically come together in their ranges again, occasional individuals might confuse members of the other species and breed; the progeny, if any, is sterile or largely so. Since such individuals produce few or no progeny, they and their genotypes are eliminated by natural selection. Within the variability of both populations, the cases of "mistaken identity" will most likely occur among the individuals with morphological and ecological counterparts in the other species. The result is that those individuals in each species that look less similar to the members of the other species produce more viable offspring. Consequently the two species will tend to look more different as time goes by. Such a phenomenon has been called "character displacement." Since character displacement is possible only where two species overlap, the populations living separately will be less distinct than those living together. Furthermore, since animals actively choose their mates, which is not the case among plants, the phenomenon will be more obvious among the former, although structures that impede fertilization by the wrong species may develop among plants.

Character displacement is illustrated by two species of rock nuthatches, *Sitta neumayer* and *Sitta tephronota*. The former species ranges from the Balkans eastward through the western half of Iran, and the latter ranges from Turkestan west to Armenia. The two species overlap in several sectors of Iran. They are very similar to each other in their separate zones, but they diverge in the zones of overlap where *S. neumayer* shows a distinct reduction in overall size, beak length, and the intensity of a prominent facial stripe, characters that are unchanged in *S. tephronota*.

Hybridization in Plants and Animals

So far we have been assuming that two breeding populations will be completely intersterile or completely interfertile, and such is usually the case. But hybridization between two species in nature yielding viable progeny is a known, although uncommon, phenomenon.

In hybridization, we usually assume that if two populations interbreed, eventually the two gene pools will completely mix so that in the last analysis, only one integrated breeding population will survive. But we know today that there are mechanisms that allow populations of different species to hybridize occasionally, but prevent them from becoming swamped. If one wonders why we consider those two populations as distinct species, one is in good company, since it is one of the knottiest problems of biology to decide how much interbreeding can take place before two populations are considered one rather than two species.

Hybridization is rather frequent among the higher plants, but is rare among the vertebrates. Following Ernst Mayr we can distinguish five main types. We have to remember though that these are not distinct categories and that there are intermediate situations.

1. The occasional crossing of sympatric species resulting in the production of hybrid individuals that are inviable or sterile and therefore do not backcross with the parental species.
2. The production of more or less fertile hybrids between sympatric species, some of which backcross to one or both parental species.
3. The formation of a secondary zone of contact and of partial interbreeding between two formerly isolated populations that failed to acquire complete reproductive isolation during the preceding period of geographic isolation.
4. The complete local breakdown of reproductive isolation between two sympatric species, resulting in the formation of hybrid swarms that may include the total range of variability of the parental species.
5. The production of a new species as the result of hybridization and subsequent doubling of the chromosomes (allopolyploidy).

The first category is of no consequence, and natural selection will take care of the hybrids and their parents. We have already discussed allopolyploidy, and the fourth category produces total swamping between the parental types. Hybridization of the second and third categories, known as introgression, will be considered now.

Interspecific hybrids will occasionally be formed that are almost totally sterile. In plants they will often not produce any viable seed, but they will produce some fertile pollen. This pollen can fertilize individuals of the parental species. In other cases, the hybrids are fertile, but they are not adapted to grow in the ecological conditions to which their parents are adapted. Two species of sage studied by Epling, *Salvia apiana* and *S. mellifera,* occur together over thousands of square miles in the coastal regions of southern California. The species are reproductively isolated, but in areas where the habitat has been disturbed by man, hybrid swarms are formed, which then backcross to the parents. Anderson has investigated two species of spiderwort, *Tradescantia caniculata* and *T. subaspera,* which grow together in the Ozark region, the former on rocky slopes in full sun and the latter on rich soil in deep shade. But in ravines and on gradually intergrading cliffs, intermediate habitats are found. On these areas grow hybrids between the two species that also produce backcrosses to the parental species. To understand why the two species maintain their identity in the face of hybridization, we have to take natural selection into account. The hybrids are obviously not well adapted to either of the two major habitats and are short-lived. The backcrosses will not be as well adapted as the pure species and will be selected against. The integrity of the species is therefore preserved by selection. But if the number of hybrids were to become very large—for example, as a result of man's activities in disturbing the habitat—the chances of a plant of either species not getting pollen from hybrids decreases, and eventually most, if not all, plants will be hybrids or backcrosses. Thus the fate of two species that hybridize will depend on the amount of interbreeding and the degree of genetic and ecological sterility of the hybrids and the backcrosses.

Isolation and Sterility

In defining species, we have emphasized breeding relationships rather than morphological similarities, although we indicated that in most instances the correspondence between morphological like-ness and degree of interbreeding is high. Although members of dif-ferent species do not interbreed, they sometimes can, and numerous instances of hybridization are a witness to it. The effectiveness of the isolation barrier is consequently of fundamental importance.

The most effective barrier is, of course, complete genetic isolation —that is, the male gamete fails to fertilize the female gamete. Genetic isolation can be brought about by a few major genic changes, but as a rule it is the result of the accumulation of several small genic and chromosomal mutations. Given enough time since their separation from a common ancestor, all species will tend to develop genetic isolation.

In addition to genetic isolation there are other mechanisms that apparently can evolve at a faster rate. They are not always as foolproof as genetic isolation is, but since they keep closely related species from breeding they are probably of greater evolutionary significance.

In animals behavioral characteristics play a leading role. Most vertebrates, insects, and crustaceans have evolved elaborate be-havioral mechanisms by which members of different sexes of the same species recognize each other. These involve so-called display mechanisms, in which either the male or the female goes through a specific type of behavior, which often involves the display of certain parts of the body. The member of the opposite sex, if it belongs to the same species, will react to this display by behaving in a species-specific manner, which in turn will be followed by a reaction by the other partner. This can go on several times and over quite a long period before mating takes place, or it can be short and fast. Studies have shown that display behavior evolves in the same way that morphological structures do and that closely related species will have similar behavior. It can therefore be used also as a characteristic in classifying animals, as well as a clue to possible barriers to crossing.

Ecological isolation is a mechanism best observed in plants. In this case two closely related species that grow in different environments can produce offspring, but the hybrids will not be able to grow, since they are not adapted to the environments of either parent. This is well illustrated by several species of oaks. Many oaks are interfertile and hybrids are occasionally found. Such is the case with four Texas species: *Quercus mohriana, Q. havardi, Q. grisea,* and *Q. stellata,* studied by C. H. Muller. These four species are kept distinct because they grow in very distinct soil types—namely, limestone, sand, igneous outcrops, and clay respectively—and the few hybrids between them are confined to the zones where the soil types come into contact.

Another type of isolation is temporal isolation. The breeding seasons of two species of animals or plants do not coincide. This type is rather common in plants. Another type of isolation mechanism in plants is produced by specific pollinators, which visit only one kind of flower, so that they insure that the pollen of that plant is carried only to a plant of the same species. The orchid family provides the best example of this type of isolation, and the elaborate floral structures of orchids are often adaptations to attract only one type of insect and to exclude the others. These mechanisms were selected, no doubt, for efficiency of pollination, and probably in isolation, but they now are also performing an isolating function.

The nature of the isolating mechanisms and the numerous instances of hybridization should serve as fair warning about the dangers of a too rigid application of the breeding and sterility criteria in the definition of species. As is true in other aspects of science, so also here the best we can hope for is an approximation that statistically will correspond with the observed facts.

Suggested Further Reading

Anderson, E. *Introgressive Hybridization.* New York: Wiley, 1949.

Epling, C. "Natural Hybridization of *Salvia apiana* and *S. mellifera.*" *Evolution, 1*:69–78, 1947.

Grant, Karen A., and V. Grant. "Mechanical Isolation of *Salvia apiana* and *Salvia mellifera* (*Labiatae*)." *Evolution, 18*:196–212, 1964.

Lewis, H., and P. H. Raven. "Rapid Evolution in Clarkia." *Evolution, 12*:319–336, 1958.

Mayr, E. "Species Concepts and Definitions." In E. Mayr (ed.), *The Species Problem*. Washington, D.C.: American Association for the Advancement of Science, 1957.

————. *Animal Species and Evolution*. Cambridge: Belknap Press of Harvard University Press, 1963 (especially Chapters 2–6).

Muller, C. H. "Ecological Control of Hybridization in Quercus: A Factor in the Mechanism of Evolution." *Evolution, 6*:147–161, 1952.

6

Sex, Behavior, and the Breeding System

In Chapter 3 we reviewed the role of recombination. It was shown that although no new genetic information (an exclusive role of mutation) is provided by recombination, it is the major source of variability in the population. It was assumed that genes were independent bodies. We have since seen that this is not so, that genes are situated on chromosomes, and consequently that genes on the same chromosome are linked. This, it was shown, restricts recombination somewhat. The role of crossing-over in reducing the effect of linkage was also discussed. Chromosomes are carried by individual organisms, and selection acts on the phenotypes of individuals, and only through them on the genotypes. Furthermore organisms aggregate into breeding populations, and interbreeding takes place only among members of the same species. All these factors, and many others, affect recombination and consequently play a major role in evolution.

In this chapter, some of the mechanisms that influence the amount of variability through their effect on recombination and their relation to the environment and the phenotype are discussed.

Factors Limiting and Affecting Recombination

Table 6·1 shows the major factors that regulate the amount of recombination. We have already discussed the role of chromosome number and of crossing-over in affecting recombination (Chapter 4) and the effect of gene flow (Chapter 3). The effect of the length of generation is quite obvious. If the number of recombinations is given by the formula (page 26):

$$\left[\frac{r\,(r+1)}{2} \right]^n$$

the number of recombinants in a unit of time (that is, per year) is obtained by multiplying the number of recombinations by the number of generations (N) in a year:

$$\left[\frac{r\,(r+1)}{2} \right]^n \times N$$

Other factors being equal, an animal with two generations a year will produce twice as many recombinants as an animal with only one generation a year.

TABLE 6·1

Factors That Regulate the Amount of Recombination

1. Chromosome number
2. Frequency of crossing-over
3. Gene flow
4. Length of generation
5. Population size
6. Breeding system
7. Incompatibility system
8. Crossability barriers and external isolating mechanisms

Source: Adapted from Grant, *Cold Spring Harbor Symposia on Quantitative Biology,* 23:329, 1958.

The length of generation has another important effect. Not all the offspring will survive to adulthood. In most natural situations on the average the number surviving is roughly equivalent to the number of organisms dying. If the species is a long-lived one, the rate of turnover is a slow one. But long-lived organisms have a chance of producing many more offspring than short-lived ones. It follows, then, that a much smaller proportion of the offspring survives to adulthood in a long-lived organism than in a short-lived one. An extreme example is the sequoias. If we assume that there are as many sequoias as possible in the area now occupied by them, the rate of replacement is about 1 offspring per sequoia every 500 to 1,000 years, while the number of seeds produced by one plant in that span of time is several million. The life-span is very short in most animals, exceeding two years in only a very small number of species. Among plants extremely great ages are known, not only among trees, but even in many kinds of herbs that reproduce vegetatively.

The larger the population the greater the possibility of storing genetic variability. In the extreme case of a population formed by two organisms there can be at most 4 different alleles for each gene and the potential of forming by sexual reproduction 10 different combinations for each gene in the following generations. In a population with three individuals there is a maximum of 6 alleles for each gene and a potential of forming 21 different combinations; with 4 individuals, 8 alleles and 36 combinations; with 5, 10 and 55; with 10, 20 and 210; and with n individuals there can be a maximum of $2n$ alleles and a potential of forming $n(n + 1)/2$ recombinants (see Chapter 3 for the derivation of this formula).

In no known case is a population heterozygous for each genic locus, but the larger the population, other factors being equal, the greater the probability of forming new combinations, and more variability may be present.

Breeding Systems

Not all organisms possess the same mode of reproduction. The different mechanisms employed are referred to as breeding systems.

Table 6·2 lists the major breeding systems of plants and animals. Asexual systems are those where no recombination takes place. Since in this type of reproduction each plant or animal reproduces its own kind without dependence on others, the reproductive mechanism itself is very efficient. In obligate apomicts (plants that produce seed without fertilization) the only new source of variability is gene mutation, and unless the generation time is very short, as in bacteria (see Chapter 3), the population will be very homogeneous genetically. Obligate asexuality is very rare, probably because the resultant highly homozygous populations are eliminated in the course of time when environmental conditions change.

In certain insects, particularly the aphids, there is an alternation of a sexual generation (usually in the fall) with asexual ones (in the spring and summer). Also in some plants that usually are asexual, occasional sexual crosses occur (not necessarily tied to the seasons as in animals). In this way there is still the possibility of genetic

recombination, coupled with the advantages of asexuality. Anybody
who has to fight aphids on his roses knows how fast and efficiently
aphids reproduce!

Several mechanisms exist that regulate the amount of inbreeding
in sexually reproducing organisms. True inbreeding is possible only
in hermaphroditic organisms. Obligatory, self-fertilizing herma-
phrodites are rare in the animal kingdom, and although more

TABLE 6·2

Major Breeding Systems in Plants and Animals

A. Asexual:

Parthenogenesis and apomixis	Seasonal (animals)	
	Facultative (plants)	
	Pseudogamy (mostly plants, some animals)	
	Obligate (plants and animals)	
Vegetative reproduction	With or	mostly plants, some animals
	without sexual reproduction	some animals and plants

B. Sexual:

Complete inbreeding (plants and a few animals)
Close inbreeding (plants and animals)

Outbreeding	Animals	monogamy	with or without numerical inequality of the sexes
		polygamy	
		polygyny	
		promiscuity	
	Plants	dioecism	
		heterostyly	
		protandry, protogyny	
		mechanical prevention of self pollination	
		multiallelic genetic self-incompatibility	

frequent in the plant kingdom, they are relatively rare among plants
too. Most animals have individuals of different sexes, which assures
outbreeding. While most plants are hermaphroditic, many mechanisms exist that prevent the sperm from fertilizing the egg of the
same plant. Some of the major ones are listed in Table 6·2. In
heterostylous plants there are two types of flowers: in some the styles
are longer than the stamens, and in others the stamens are longer
than the styles (Figure 6·1). Pollen of short stamens is normally

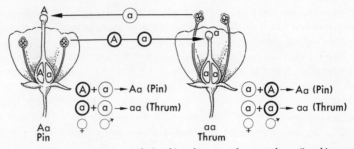

Figure 6·1. Diagram crossing relationships between heterostylous (in this case, distylous) plants. An a pollen produced by the pin plant reacts on the thrum style as if it were **A**. Note that both pin and thrum plants yield exactly ½ pins and ½ thrums in their progeny.

viable only on short styles, and pollen of long stamens on long styles, thereby insuring outbreeding.

Protandrous flowers are those in which the pollen matures ahead of the female organs, and protogynous flowers are those in which the female organs ripen before the pollen. Again here there is a reduced possibility of self-fertilization. Then there are various mechanical contrivances that keep pollen away from the stigmas.

The most common mechanism to prevent self-fertilization in plants is genetic incompatibility (Figure 6·2). A self-incompatibility gene, called the S gene, is the controlling factor. The S gene has many alleles, referred to as S^1, S^2, S^3, . . . , S^n, of which there are

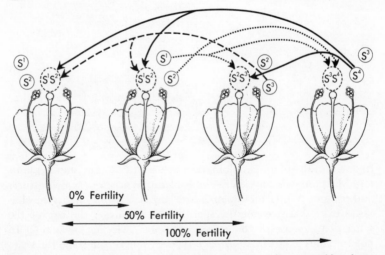

Figure 6·2. Diagram of crossing relationships between self-incompatible plants. Unbroken circles show pollen grains; broken circles show genotypes of styles.

often more than 30, 50, or even a 100 in a population. A plant will not ordinarily accept pollen with the same allele as itself. So if a plant is of the constitution S^1S^2, it will not be fertilized by S^1 or S^2 pollen, which are, of course, the two types of pollen the plant produces (it should be remembered that the pollen is haploid and meiosis has preceded its formation—see Chapter 4). An S^1S^2 plant resists fertilization by any other S^1S^2 plant in the population, and when crossed with an S^1S^3 plant, it is the S^3 pollen that will be viable on the S^1S^2 plant. The alleles determining self-incompatibility apparently produce their effect by controlling the rate of pollen tube growth or even pollen germination. The stylar tissue produces a substance (probably an antigenlike product) that inhibits or drastically slows down the growth of the pollen tubes of the same genetic constitution.

Types of Recombination Systems

It should be clear by now that recombination is the result of a chain of processes that begins with gene mutation and continues through the sexual cycle. Genes are associated in chromosomes that restrict recombination. Individual organisms are associated in breeding populations and species that set a limit to recombination. The genes of a whale cannot be recombined with those of a walrus. Consequently only a fraction of the potentialities of recombination are ever realized in nature.

We have seen that even the fraction of attainable recombination varies, depending primarily on the breeding system but also on factors such as the size of the population, frequency of crossing over, and chromosome number. Following a proposal of the American geneticist Hampton Carson, we can classify organisms according to their recombination system into those with a relatively open system, those with a restricted system, and those with a closed system. A closed recombination system exemplified by obligate parthenogenetic or apomictic organisms is one where no recombination takes place; a restricted recombination system is one which imposes strong barriers to recombination such as in facultative apomicts (normally asexual plants that nevertheless can breed sexually) or close inbreeders; while an open recombination system is one where a large number of the potential recombinants are normally produced.

We may ask ourselves why these variations in recombinations exist. Why do certain organisms have a closed recombination system and others an open one, sometimes even in closely related species? The answer is to be found in the adjustment species have to make between immediate fitness and flexibility. By immediate fitness is meant the necessity of all populations to produce enough offspring to maintain their numbers. Flexibility refers to the production of new recombinants.

It is advantageous for a population to be variable—that is, to possess many diverse recombinants. In this way there always will be some genotypes capable of adapting to new situations, both in space (when new habitats are occupied) and in time (as the environment changes over the centuries). But there is a price to pay for a large amount of recombination: a large number of the offspring will be ill adapted and therefore will be eliminated by natural selection. A species (such as the *Sequoia* tree or a *Drosophila* female which lays about 300 eggs) that produces a number of zygotes far in excess of those that can survive is not affected. But this might represent too great a load for other species. They will not be able to maintain themselves and might become extinct unless a mechanism develops that restricts recombination. It should be remembered that natural selection favors the population that produces, generation after generation, the highest number of surviving progeny, regardless of the recombination system.

Why don't all species that produce a small surplus of "dispensable" progeny become parthenogenetic then? This method would assure immediate fitness (though at the expense of flexibility). Probably because an asexually reproducing population or species relies only on gene mutation for any new variability, and in organisms that have only a few generations a year at most (the case with the overwhelming majority of species), this mechanism does not produce enough new changes to cope with the changing environment, and the species sooner or later will become unadapted and consequently extinct.

We have mentioned briefly the role of the environment, and we will come back to it in the next chapter. If the ecological situation in which an organism lives is very specialized, only a specialized type of organism will be able to survive, and the population will tend to be rather uniform. Less specialized environments, such as a subtropical forest, permit the existence of more variable populations. The environment undoubtedly plays a major role in selecting the recombination system.

An interesting example is the plant genus *Myosurus*, the mousetails, studied by D. Stone in California. These plants grow in the vernal pools of the Central Valley of California. The vernal pools are small depressions in the plains, underlaid by alkaline clay soils. During the rainy fall and winter months the pools overflow with water, but during the dry spring months the water evaporates until they become totally dry in April or early May. Studies revealed from four to nine different biotypes of *Myosurus* growing together in one vernal pool. These biotypes were true-breeding, but proved to be interfertile when hybridized. The plants are self-fertilizing due to a peculiar development of the flower (Figure 6·3). In one species, *Myosurus sessilis,* the receptacle of the flower continues to develop and produces new pistils at the top. These can only be fertilized by foreign pollen. Thus, this peculiar plant has a mechanism by which some seeds can be cross-pollinated, although most are self-pollinated.

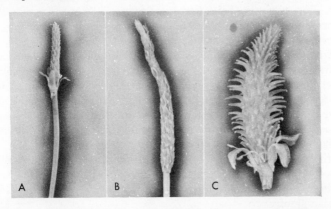

Figure 6·3. A: *Myosurus minimus.* Flower shortly after emergence. Petals can be seen on the sides of the receptacle, the receptive stigmas are seen on the upper half. **B:** Same species with scattered seed on upper half due to incomplete fertilization. **C:** *Myosurus sessilis.* In this species new achenes are formed at the tip after emergence (in the previous one, maturation took place from top to base). Sepals and stamens are visible at the base; developing achenes are visible at the tip. [Photo courtesy of Dr. D. E. Stone.]

The mousetails live in an extreme environment. This environment permits only the growth of highly specialized plants. *Myosurus* is one of these. Its closed recombination system assures a crop of highly specialized plants generation after generation. But flexibility and variability are also favored as witnessed by up to nine biotypes in the same pool. Hence a mechanism has been selected that maintains some outbreeding.

We do not know if recombination systems such as that of the mousetails are frequent or a rare exception. Very few organisms have been studied in such detail as these. Much more investigation is needed in this area and no doubt will yield surprising results.

Another factor that affects recombination in animals is behavior. Behavior has other important evolutionary roles, and therefore deserves separate attention.

Broadly speaking, behavior is what an animal does, the overt actions of an animal. What an animal does, or avoids doing, must to a large extent determine his survival, both as an individual and as a species, in which case there is a definite selective advantage for the species in genetically fixing behavior that is beneficial. Consequently behavior must be under strong selective pressures and must evolve in the same way that a morphological structure does. But insofar as behavior leaves no fossil record (although we can infer something about the behavior of ancient animals by examining their bones, burrows, and so forth) there is no absolute proof for this assertion. But there is strong circumstantial evidence.

Study of the evolution of behavior and the use of behavioral characteristics in systematics is a relatively new field. Observations on the behavior of animals have, of course, been made and recorded for a long time, but either they were not interpreted at all, or they were considered anthropomorphically, in terms of purposeful behavior. The development of a conceptual framework that interprets behavior in terms of survival, and which is as much concerned with the genetic basis as with the description of the mechanical aspects of it, has produced a small revolution in this field. The study of behavior is a rapidly expanding and highly promising field of human inquiry.

Although behavior usually involves an overt action, it arises from within the organism and obviously involves all sorts of internal physiological and biochemical mechanisms. Certain types of behavior may occur in direct response to an external stimulus, and all of the behavior of the lower animals is of this type. But even in these instances the mechanisms of response are internal. In the higher animals there is behavior without any immediate outside stimulus, although it always involves previous experience with external stimuli. Such behavior requires complex associative processes and usually also a memory, whether conscious or not, and is in most instances dependent on a well-developed nervous system.

All behavior, whether it is a response to a direct external stimulus or not, involves and is strongly influenced and in large part determined by the receptor-conductor-effector organs (senses, nervous system, brain, muscles, and so on) and further by associative mechanisms when these are present in the conductor system. This explains in part why different animals respond differently to similar stimuli, and a great deal can be learned about behavior by studying the physiology and anatomy of the sensory mechanisms of an animal. We will assume that the reader has some familiarity with this aspect of the subject and will concentrate on the role behavior has played in the evolution of the animal kingdom and how behavior itself is modified by natural selection.

Throughout our discussion we have been emphasizing that animal and plant populations become adapted to their environment through natural selection. The organization of living beings reflects this adaptation at every level, from the morphology and anatomy to the physiology. Behavior is the visible and direct expression of adaptation. In the last analysis all the structures of an animal are adaptive in terms of what an animal does. But while the anatomy and physiology of an animal are relatively easy to understand in terms of their genetic determination and in terms of the underlying chemical reactions, behavior is much more complex.

Behavioral characteristics are genetically determined, and they are transmitted from generation to generation in the same way as morphological or physiological characteristics. Behavioral changes are dependent on the appearance of favorable mutations and recombinations and on the action of selection.

On the other hand, behavior is undoubtedly goal-directed. A certain action is performed to obtain food, avoid a predator, assure a mate, or protect the young. Populations whose individual members behave in such a way that they assure the production of a large number of young surviving to adulthood will be selected. But it should not be concluded that this purposeful "drive" of individuals "directs" evolution. A tiger is incapable of surviving on grass. Its teeth and digestive apparatus do not permit him to do so. Nor would a tiger eat grass, even if starving.

Isolation and Breeding Behavior

In the previous chapter reference was made to the important role played by breeding behavior in keeping animal species isolated. The abundance of interspecific hybrids in plants and their rarity in animals may be related in some degree to lack of behavior in plants. Observation and analysis of the behavioral elements that operate as isolating mechanisms show that closely related species possess quite similar behavior. These studies also indicate that the different mechanisms involved in breeding behavior have evolved by the accumulation of small modifications. Nevertheless some general patterns and

types of breeding behavior can be discerned. The following classification is that of Herman T. Spieth of the University of California.

For two opposite-sexed individuals of the same species to mate,
the first necessary requirement is that they be in physical proximity
so that they are able to recognize each other. Most populations of
animals occupy a relatively small territory, and furthermore within
that area prefer and are attracted by similar elements in the environment. Most insects and some vertebrates mate at the feeding ground
to which both sexes have been attracted. The breeding behavior in
these animals is short, fast, and at least to human eyes quite indiscriminate. This type of behavior has been called the *basic type*.
The stimulus is usually direct physical contact, but in some animals
some primitive means of attracting the other sex also are found.
Female nocturnal moths produce odors, and female mosquitoes
make sounds that attract the males. In crickets it is the male that
makes the sounds that attract the other sex. There are also in some
species primitive displays of bright colors or special structures, but
this is rare in the basic type. The stimulus is normally direct physical
contact.

In some aquatic species a still more primitive type is found.
Under the stimulus of environmental factors, both sexes attain
simultaneous sexual readiness. One or a few individuals (usually
males) will spawn spontaneously and in this way stimulate the rest
of the population to do the same. This has been called the *sedentary
aquatic type.*

Many vertebrates establish a territory that they defend against
the invasion of any individual of the same species. Typically the
male establishes the territory and after pair bonds have been formed
between the male and a female, both individuals defend the territory. The pair may be established for the duration of the breeding
season or on a more permanent basis. Animals showing this type
of breeding behavior, called *territorial type,* differ from the basic
type in that pair bonds of some duration are formed and in the
possession of three strong behavioral elements, called drives. These
are (1) the sexual or mating drive, (2) aggression or fighting
drive, and (3) fleeing or escape drive. The interaction of these three
mutually antagonistic elements of behavior has resulted in highly
ritualized and complex breeding behavior, so that it sometimes takes
hours before copulation takes place. Characteristically, courting consists of a series of actions, which are triggered and in turn trigger
the actions of the opposite sex, such as displacement actions, threat
postures, displays of body parts. These complicated behaviors serve
as strong isolating mechanisms, since if the reciprocal actions do not

correspond, courtship is immediately interrupted and copulation does not take place.

Behavior similar to the territorial type is shown in the *predatory nonterritorial* type. To this group belong the spiders, which, although they do not establish a territory, possess the same involved breeding behavior and also show the three basic drives explained above.

Some animal species form gregarious assemblages at the time of courtship. The males congregate at a special place that the females normally frequent, or the females may be attracted by the presence of the males. Mating behavior is complex and often extends over a considerable period of time. The lek birds are a characteristic example of this type of breeding behavior, which consequently has been termed *lek type*. Evolutionarily, this type is an artificial assemblage derived from different behavioral types. In the case of the lek birds, for example, it has evolved from a territorial type, but in the case of crabs of the genus *Uca* or of *Drosophila* fruit flies, it is derived from the basic type. All groups nevertheless show two common characteristics: (1) the males are promiscuous and will try to mate several times in a season, and (2) the breeding behavior of the males is hypertrophied compared with the males of related but nongregarious species. The elaborate and colorful feathers and display mechanisms of birds of paradise are a case in point.

There are, of course, many variations in detail in all these breeding types. In general there is a trend to more elaborate mechanisms, which constitute better isolating mechanisms between species and, because they minimize the chances of hybridization, are also more efficient. The formation of longer-lasting bonds in the higher vertebrates particularly also assures a better care of the young.

Two other trends are worth mentioning. In primitive animals the ripening of the gametes is synchronized by the environment. In more advanced animals there is in addition an effect of the individuals of the two sexes upon each other. In many birds pair formation often precedes actual insemination by a considerable time, during which specific ceremonies are repeated many times by the pair. These ceremonies apparently keep the pair together, but also lead to the production of hormones that synchronize the production of gametes. This interaction is another mechanism that isolates the animal from members of other species.

Recognition of the other sex sometimes also presents a problem. Males of many insects cannot recognize the other sex until it has tapped the other insect and it has responded. *Sarcophaga* male flies will attempt copulation with other *Sarcophaga* males and with individuals of other species. Tapping the wrong individual often produces a scuffle, but with no harmful consequences. But with strongly armed animals, such as spiders, a scuffle could be harmful. In spiders, therefore, mechanisms have evolved by which males can recognize the opposite sex without prior physical contact. Such mechanisms are of obvious selective advantage.

Sexual Selection

If for each female in the population there are several available males, the female may choose the one of her liking. If one male is capable of driving away other males either by threats or by actual combat and as a result manages to fertilize one or more females, the successful male will produce more offspring (in extreme cases to the exclusion of all other males). Those characteristics which make the male (or the female) more attractive or more threatening and contribute to his success will be of adaptive significance and will be selected. This is the essence of the theory of sexual selection presented for the first time by Charles Darwin in 1871 in his book *The Descent of Man* to account for the differences between male and female found in many species of animals, which do not appear to be of general adaptive significance.

In his original presentation, Darwin stressed combat as a very important selective force—antlers in deer, wing and leg spurs in many birds, horns in stag beetles. Actual combat occurs in many instances (although so far it has not been observed among stag beetles), but display of aggressive structures such as horns or tusks, or behavior such as raising of fur or feathers to give an appearance of greater size as a threat without actual combat, may play a more important role than fighting. Overaggressive behavior may reduce rather than increase fitness, as is the case in many species of elk, where actual combat may eliminate both aggressors or, at best, will allow other males to run away with the does while the fight goes on. Structures of use in combat may evolve consequently with little actual combat, at least between members of the same species. Nevertheless, we should not assume that every difference between males and females is of a threatening nature.

Intrasexual selection will advance with the greatest momentum in species where the competition between members of one sex is keenest. Darwin perceived this and therefore attached great significance to the mating system of a species. Strict monogamy with numerical equality between the sexes is the one system in which intrasexual selection will be ineffective, provided that the mating takes place for at least the length of the breeding season. All other mating types—polygamy, promiscuity, and numerical inequality of the sexes—will allow for at least some intrasexual selection. Since the most common mating systems are monogamy with an excess of males, and polygyny (one male fertilizing many females), intra-male selection should be more common than intrafemale selection, and such is the case. In these systems, males that conquer and ward off by threat or combat other males, or possess characters that will attract more females, leave a greater progeny to inherit their features.

Display behavior between sexes, which is important in keeping interfertile species isolated, will be reinforced by sexual selection. Males or females that can elicit, by their display behavior, fast responses in the other sex will have a selective advantage over other individuals of their same sex, and their behavior will be perpetuated in the species. Thus sexual selection and interspecific natural selection reinforce each other. At this point it should be emphasized that "choosing" of a mate should not be interpreted as conscious selection by one mate of "beneficial" characteristics in his partner. Rather it is the effectiveness of the response elicited by the displaying animal from its potential partner that is responsible for the "choosing," and the more effective the display, the greater the chances of success and of perpetuating the particular genotype and of increasing its frequency in the population.

Sexual selection reinforces natural selection also in favoring specialized, relatively invariable structures and associated behavior. If a certain combination of colored feathers is particularly advantageous, genes, called modifier genes, which tend to fix this structure and make it invariable, will be selected. Thus sexual selection in part contributes to decrease the morphological variability of animals and in turn is only possible among organisms that have a relatively fixed and stable development.

Do Plants Have Behavior?

Plants do not have behavior in the usual sense of the word, although certain tropisms, such as geotropism (the tendency of the root to grow down) or heliotropism (the tendency of the shoots to grow up toward the light) or nastic movements (orientation movements of leaves and flowers) have been interpreted as behavior. Plants do have some simple receptor and effector mechanisms, but they lack conductor organs and any kind of associative behavior.

Although plants lack behavior, the evolution of the flower-pollinator mechanism illustrates very nicely the operation of the selective process. Flowering plants depend on foreign agents, particularly insects, to carry pollen from one plant to the next. Consequently the flower has evolved in such a way that it is capable of attracting a pollinator and dusting it with pollen in such a way that when it visits a flower of the same species it will brush the pollen against the style and pollinate it. Attracting an insect and dusting it with pollen so that it will pollinate another flower could be interpreted as purposeful behavior. But obviously a plant is incapable of purposeful behavior. The accumulation of small favorable mutations has produced the flower, just as the accumulation of small favorable mutations accounts for the complex behavioral patterns of animals. A lion ant builds a trap for its prey, an orchid attracts a bee with a combination of scent and color. Because of the operations involved and a certain degree of choice as to place and time, we think of the lion ant actions as purposeful. They are so only in the way orchid "behavior" is purposeful. In terms of the evolution of behavior, the determining factor is the selection of structures and actions that contribute to the production of the highest number of surviving progeny.

Another interesting parallel between flowering plants and animals is in the development of pollinator-attracting mechanisms that are species-specific. Primitive flowers are visited by insects that are indiscriminate in their taste for flowers. These are as likely to visit a flower of a different species as of the same species they visited last. More advanced flowers by and large tend to (1) attract a specific type or even species of insect, or if visited by many, dust with pollen only some; and (2) attract and dust insects, such as bees, that visit one kind of flowers at a time. In this latter case, the pollinator acts as an effective isolating mechanism, insuring that the pollen falls only on the right kind of stigma.

The Evolution of Sex

The primary biological significance of sexual reproduction is that it achieves recombination of the genetic material and in this way increases the amount of genetic variability in the population. Sexuality so defined exists in all major groups of organisms with the exception of the blue-green algae, where so far it has not been observed. The selective forces that brought sexuality about, as well as the chemical and physiological processes underlying it, are varied and complex, and many of the evolutionary aspects are only conjectural, since no kind of a permanent record has been left. We will try here to summarize briefly some of the salient points of this fascinating subject.

Sexuality may have been a property of the very first organisms, or it may have evolved at a later stage. According to the latter view, the first organisms were strictly asexual, relying on mutation to provide genetic variability. When the generation time is short, mutation can supply enough variability to cope with a mildly changing environment. Cellular fusion under this view would have been the origin of sexuality, with selection favoring other changes to improve the efficiency of the union, culminating in formation of gametes and fertilization. Meiosis must have developed parallel to sexuality in this scheme.

The other view pushes the advent of genetic recombination back to the first forms of life. The DNA molecules at this early stage might have been recombined by some kind of infectionlike mechanism resulting in the formation of better and more efficient molecules. As the different features of the cell evolved and became an integral part of the organism, mechanisms protecting and insuring recombination must have evolved. The most likely mechanism is fusion of all cellular contents. Primitive cells probably could have tolerated such fusion because of the simplicity of their enzyme systems. Eventually such promiscuous fusion would result in too much genetic variation, and methods of controlling and regulating the fusion process were evolved. They in turn permitted the development of a more complex but more efficient cellular metabolism.

A primitive cell can be visualized as containing a large number of DNA molecules, each duplicating more or less independently of the others. Selection probably favored the association of these molecules into larger, more synchronized units to assure a greater metabolic efficiency. In turn, the higher degree of order would have permitted division of the cell into equal parts. Formation of chromosomes and concomitant linkage of functional DNA units, genes, provided for an efficient mechanism for exact transmission of the genetic information to the daughter nuclei and for a higher precision of metabolic activity. Linkage also reduced recombination, increasing the need for a sexual mechanism that could function under the new conditions. Mitosis, meiosis, and fertilization probably evolved more or less simultaneously at this stage (Figure 6·4).

A later development has been the attainment of diploidy. The greatest likelihood is that meiosis followed fertilization in primitive organisms as is still the case. The evolution of diploidy probably occurred because of the immediate advantages of genetic heterozygosity, which allows the buffering of nonadaptive mutations (recessiveness) and allows for heterozygous superiority and a correlated increase in genetic variability. Delaying meiosis would allow for the formation of a diploid organism alternating with a haploid organism until eventually meiosis takes place just prior to fertilization.

Finally some kind of mechanism was selected to prevent fusion between two gametes produced by the same individual. One such mechanism is the one found in the great majority of animals and in

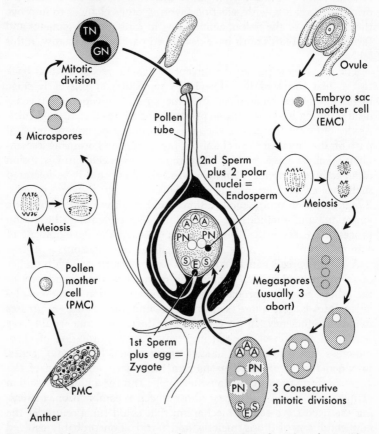

Figure 6·4. Schematic representation of gametogenesis in flowering plants with a normal type of embryo sac development. Shaded cells are haploid (gametophyte). TN = tube nucleus; GN = generative nucleus; S = synergids; E = egg cell; PN = embryo-sac mother cell.

a few plants, in which two kinds of gametes, eggs and sperms, are formed by different individuals in the species (Figure 6·5). Such a mechanism is possible only in diploid organisms. In effect a factor (gene or chromosome) is present in double dose in one kind of individual and in single dose in the other. The heterozygous individuals produce gametes with and without the factor in the same amounts, which in turn produces descendants having the sexual factor in two or one dose (see Chapter 4).

In haploid organisms the mechanism to prevent self-fertilization involves a series of alleles such as that in which no homozygous zygote is viable. In the higher plants where a diploid organism produces both eggs and sperms a similar mechanism is operative. The diploid organism is always heterozygous, and only gametes carrying a third allele will be able to fertilize the plant. In actuality the pollen will not germinate on a style that has the same incom-

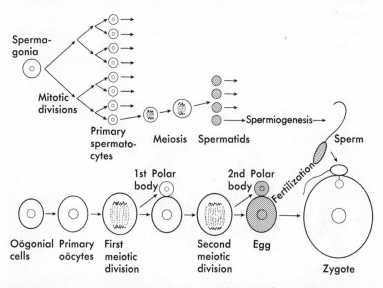

Figure 6·5. Gametogenesis and fertilization in higher animals. Only the gametes are haploid; meiosis is followed by fertilization.

patibility allele. As we have seen, the incompatibility locus is usually referred to as the S locus, and it is possible that it consists of two units that control the production of pollen and stylar antigens.

From the information presented so far, we can see that the development of sexuality illustrates the interaction of different levels of organization within the organism and the correlation between intrinsic and extrinsic factors. On account of environmental fluctuations and climatic changes, organisms have to possess ways to change with the environment. In very simple primitive organisms this could be accomplished in a random and relatively haphazard way. More complex organisms have highly integrated developmental systems that are easily upset. Under such situations the introduction of foreign genes is likely to have a deleterious effect. Consequently barriers that keep foreign genes out of the gene pool are selected. But more complex organisms mean also longer generations, and the species runs the risk of becoming too uniform if too strong a barrier to recombination is erected. And so, the evolution of the sexual mechanism reflects the many forces that enter into what we call the adaptation of an organism to its environment. Let us now briefly look at some factors of the environment.

Suggested Further Reading

Baker, H. G. "Race Formation and Reproductive Method in Flowering Plants." *Symposia Soc. Exptl. Biol.,* No. 7:114–145, 1953.

Carson, H. L. "The Species as a Field for Gene Recombination." In E. Mayr (ed.), *The Species Problem.* Washington, D.C.: Am. Ass. Adv. of Science, 1957.

Cullen, J. M. "Behavior as a Help in Taxonomy." In *Function and Taxonomic Importance of Characters in Classification.* Syst. Ass. Publ. (London), No. 3:131–140.

Grant, V. "The Regulation of Recombination in Plants." *Cold Spring Harbor Symposia Quant. Biol., 23:*337–363, 1958.

Mayr, E. "Behavior and Systematics." In A. Roe and G. G. Simpson, *Behavior and Evolution.* New Haven, Conn.: Yale University Press, 1958.

Spieth, H. T. "Behavior and Isolating Mechanisms." In A. Roe and G. G. Simpson, *Behavior and Evolution,* New Haven, Conn.: Yale University Press, 1958.

Stone, D. E. "A Unique Balanced Breeding System in the Vernal Pool Mouse-tails." *Evolution, 13:*151–174, 1959.

7

Adaptation and Environment

INDIVIDUALS, POPULATIONS, AND SPECIES do not live in a vacuum. They are surrounded and affected by, and in turn affect, the sum total of the factors composing the milieu in which they exist. This aggregation of physical, chemical, and biological factors is what we call the environment. Ecology is the branch of biology that deals with the relation between the environment and the organism. Biogeography is the study of the distribution of animals and plants on the earth and the intrinsic and extrinsic—that is, the genetic and environmental—factors that account for this distribution. It is easy to see how evolution, ecology, and biogeography are overlapping subjects that to a certain extent depend on each other for their data.

Evolution and the Ecosystem

Evolution is sometimes described as changes in the frequency of genes of a species population. Why does the frequency of genes change in a population? We have already seen that mutation, recombination, selection, and gene flow are the major factors that account for this change. But it was also demonstrated that after a certain number of generations an equilibrium between these forces is reached, and that no change in the gene frequency should occur after that, provided that mutation, recombination, gene flow, and selection remain constant or essentially so. But selection depends on the environment, and the environment is changing all the time. There are variations in environmental conditions between day and night, summer and winter, wet and dry years; there are short-term cycles of temperature and rainfall that may take a decade or a century; and there are long-term cycles of changes that take place over the millennia, such as glaciations, warming trends, drying trends. The effect of all these changes is to alter the selection coefficient s. Genes that are favored by selection today will not be favored tomorrow, and vice versa. Consequently a true equilibrium is never reached.

In addition to temporal changes in the environment, there are spatial variations. The poles are cold and inhospitable; the tropics are warm and favorable for life; mountain peaks simulate arctic temperatures but differ in soil and light conditions; the coastal areas have climates with fewer temperature extremes than interior regions; and rainfall varies widely over the surface of the earth providing a basis for deserts, grasslands, deciduous forests, and rain forests. In each of these situations selection favors different types of organisms. Thick furs are of use in the arctic but not in the tropics; large evergreen leaves are advantageous in a rain forest but not in a desert. The almost infinite multitude of different organisms we see around us is the result of different selection pressures acting on populations over millions of years. And organisms, once they have evolved, bring about more evolution by affecting the environment they live in, sometimes to the point of bringing about their own disappearance.

The totality of the dynamic situation is referred to as the ecosystem, which comprises the plants, the animals, and the physical conditions such as soil, topography, and climate, and also the interaction among all of these factors. We should not think of the ecosystem as an obligate, highly integrated relationship, as a kind of superorganism, but neither should we think of it as an aggregate of organisms with coincidental requirements. Changes in each of the factors, such as extinction of a certain species, will produce changes, sometimes very drastic ones, in the ecosystem. The overall relationships will persist, though modified somewhat.

A good example is what has happened in the western United States with deer populations. The number of deer is controlled by two major factors: the availability of food and the effect of predation, this mainly by the puma or mountain lion. The deer is a browsing animal and eats leaves and young shoots of a variety of shrubs. Early pioneers were not interested in the deer other than as a source of food. They were interested in increasing grassland for sheep. Mountain lions were also relentlessly hunted, partially because they occasionally attacked flocks of sheep, and partially because man has not yet overcome the primitive instinct that leads him to kill every predatory animal. The unlimited hunting of mountain lions and of deer led to a dwindling of their numbers, and also to an increase in shrubs, because deer were not eating them; and the increase in shrubs in turn decreased the land available for the sheep. Eventually the deer population grew very small. A more sophisticated generation of men decided that the animal should be protected. Ordinances were passed establishing hunting seasons and restricting hunting to bucks. The deer population immediately started increasing at a rapid pace, to the point that now it is very large. But no similar ordinances protecting mountain lions have been passed, so that the weak and old deer are no longer killed by their natural predator. The result is that there are too many deer for the food available. Hungry deer are destroying all available shrubs and invading good pastureland, eating grass rather than shrubs and competing with sheep. There is no doubt that as a result of these changes the ecosystem has been upset, but a new balance has been established. The proportion of plants and animals has changed, the productivity of certain lands has been altered, but no wholesale destruction of the ecosystem has taken place.

Another example is the changes brought about in New Zealand by the introduction of grazing and browsing mammals. In their absence prior to the arrival of the white man, a dense grass and shrub cover maintained the mountain slopes at a steeper angle than that at which they would have settled due to the effects of gravity and other natural forces. When introduced, large mammals destroyed the plant cover and the slopes started slipping, a process that is still taking place and which will change the New Zealand landscape somewhat. Again in this example the ecosystem has been changed, but it has acquired a new steady state.

Adaptation

Selection operates on the totality of the characters of an organism, the phenotype, and only when advantageous characteristics are associated with a particular gene combination does selection act on that gene. Every organism must be capable of coping with its environment, or it will cease to persist. There are many ways of coping with the environment. For example, if a plant lives in a desert where the economy of water is paramount, one adaptation is a reduced leaf surface and a proportional increase of the woody *1* parts to reduce the loss of water through the leaves. This is exemplified by the typical desert shrubs such as sagebrush. Or the plant can be fleshy and store water as do succulents, of which cacti are the *2* most characteristic. And finally certain desert plants are capable of growing only when it rains and water is plentiful. This last pattern *3* is followed by the colorful annual desert flowers of the American

Figure 7·1. Succulents. The succulent habit has been acquired independently by several families of flowering plants, as an adaptation to extremely dry conditions. Among them the Cactaceae (**A:** *Opuntia* sp.); Aizoaceae (**B:** *Gibbaeum petrense*); Crassulaceae (**C:** *Crassula arborea*); Euphorbiaceae (**D:** *Euphorbia splendens*).

Southwest. Their seeds germinate when it rains, and the plants grow, bloom, and produce a new crop of seeds in a matter of a few weeks, while the soil is still damp, and then they die. These three different ways of coping with their environment are some of the various adaptations of plants to dry conditions (Figure 7·1).

Adaptations are still more obvious in animals. Greyhounds and pure-bred racing horses are similarly built: long legs, relatively small bodies, narrow chests, long necks and heads. All these are adaptations to the same basic function: speed. In this case the changes have been brought about by man, but a wild cheetah also has the same basic characteristics, and the cheetah relies on swiftness to catch its prey (Figure 7·2). Adaptation is then the hereditary adjustment to the environment.

From the examples given we can infer two important generalizations: organisms, even closely related species, can adapt to the same environment in dissimilar ways; and unrelated organisms can acquire similar characteristics when adapting to the same environment. This latter phenomenon is called convergent evolution, and it can be very confusing when attempting to ascertain the relationship between two species of animals or plants, especially when they are living in widely separated areas. So, for example, plants of the family Euphorbiaceae in the African deserts have acquired many of the morphological characteristics of cacti, which are exclusively

Figure 7·2. Adaptation to speed either as a means of defence or attack (or for its own sake when selected by man), has produced a series of similar modifications in widely unrelated animals, such as long necks and legs, thin and relatively long bodies, and narrow and elongated faces. The horse (both wild horses and, particularly, man-bred racing horses), wild cheetah, greyhound, and rabbit are a few examples.

New World plants. The Tasmanian "wolf," which has similar habits to true wolves and looks quite similar to them, is not a placental mammal as are wolves, but a marsupial.

Adaptations are not only morphological, but also physiological and even behavioral. "Playing dead" by opossums is an adaptation that enables them sometimes to avoid being eaten by predators, and therefore is of selective advantage. In reality the opossum is not playing dead, but is truly immobilized due to physiological reactions that have taken place. This characteristic is genetically fixed and is transmitted to the offspring. Natural selection has favored this mechanism of defense and those combinations of genes which prevent the opossum from moving when "playing dead." Hence the control of "playing dead" is not voluntary but involuntary.

Adaptability and Homeostasis

Organisms also undergo various types of nongenetic changes in direct response to their environment. Plants in shady places grow tall and spindly, while the same plant in a sunny place becomes stouter and more fleshy. The chameleon is green when among leaves and brown when on a background of dried leaves and sticks. These noninheritable changes are called the adaptability of an organism (we referred to them in Chapter 2 as the nonhereditable component of variation). They do not play a direct role in evolution, since they cannot be transmitted. They are nevertheless of direct adaptive value to the individual. It is advantageous for the chameleon to turn green on a green background and brown on a brown background so that it is inconspicuous to its enemies and to the insects it catches for food.

The plasticity of the phenotype is relatively great in some types of organisms and slight in others. In general, plants have a much more plastic phenotype than animals, particularly higher animals. This is no doubt related in part to the fact that a plant is bound to the ground and cannot take refuge from the environment other than by morphological changes. Animals can move and restrict the environmental conditions in which they live. They respond with morphological changes (a "plantlike" way) to those conditions they cannot avoid, such as by growing long hair, accumulating fat, and hybernating in nonmigratory mammals as a response to winter.

On the other hand many animals will remain constant and stable in the face of environmental changes. This phenomenon is called physiological homeostasis. When corn plants are grown under conditions of high and low moisture, the resulting products look very different. A dachshund bred in Brazil looks the same as one bred in Germany. Homeostasis is a property of the developmental system of organisms whereby different individual developmental steps brought about by different environmental conditions lead to the same end product. For a species with highly coordinated body functions, like mammals and birds, it is probably advantageous that the body remain relatively constant. Hence they change little in response to the environment.

These various adjustments of individuals to their environment are adaptive insofar as they enable the particular species to survive in a changeable environment. But it must be remembered that unless phenotypic adjustments are inherited, they do not contribute to evolution.

Adaptation and Preadaptation

Selection will favor the development of increasingly more efficient mechanisms operating under particular conditions. Thus by selection the organism becomes more and more specialized, since specialized individuals can perform much better whatever function they are fit for. 'In human society, "specialists" are rewarded with better salaries and more secure positions; in natural situations specialized species have a better chance of survival. But there is a built-in danger in specialization; when selection pressures change, the species may have lost its flexibility to adapt to the new conditions. This will happen sooner or later because the environment is always changing. In such situations in a human society a specialist will be out of work (and his specialization will die out). In natural conditions the species will become extinct, unless the species is "preadapted" to the new situation. We say that a structure is preadapted when as a result of selection in one environment and for one function, it has developed to a point where it is able to perform a new function for which it was not selected. When the early hominids abandoned walking on all fours and became brachiators—that is, when they learned to move by swinging from tree to tree hanging by their arms—selection favored forelimbs with prehensile fingers and animals that could perhaps run over short stretches on their hindlimbs. This selection led eventually to an animal which, although not entirely erect, was more erect than his ancestors. To a certain extent this freed his forelimbs from walking and made it possible for him to learn the use of tools. We can say, then, that the forelimbs of man's ancestors were preadapted for the use of tools. The selection pressures that brought this about were related to brachiating, but when a new function was required, the structure was there. The new selection force, use of tools, reinforced and perfected the forelimbs, and probably also had a great impact on the brain and on the posture of man, but it would not have taken place unless the arms and hands were preadapted to the use of tools.

Preadaptation is an important concept, and it explains how we can have evolution and adaptation at the same time in a changing environment. It should be remembered that the fate of nonadapted individuals, populations, and species is extinction. As a result of changed environmental conditions many specialized and thriving organisms became unable to cope with their surroundings and died. Thousands of once dominant species, after flourishing sometimes for long periods, have become extinct. Examples are the dinosaurs, the giant notoungulates of South America; or among plants, the giant calamites and seed ferns, which once dominated the vegetation of the earth. In more recent times we have witnessed and are still witnessing the extinction of many animals and plants such as passenger pigeons, American bison, the pretty *Franklinia* shrub (known today only in cultivation), and many others, which are incapable of coping with an environment changed drastically by hostile man. That this is not a necessary fate of all organisms is demonstrated by such diverse organisms as wheat rusts, cockroaches, Japanese beetles, rats, and starlings, which are thriving in spite of, and in fact largely because of, man.

Evolutionary Success

An interesting question is to determine what constitutes "success" in an evolutionary sense. In a very general way, the successful population can be defined as the one that can persist in time, adjust to environmental changes, and maintain or increase its numbers. What does such a population look like? What is its breeding system, its size? Is it a very variable population or a monomorphic one? How is it affected by gene flow, by mutation, by selection? We don't know. But it would be very important to know the structure of such a population.

A first question is to ask by what parameter can "success" be measured. Geneticists, ecologists, and evolutionists are not yet united in this basic point. One classical way of approaching the problem is to use "fitness" as the measure of success. This has been the approach of the population geneticist.

Relative fitness of two genotypes is defined as the ratio of the offspring produced by them. The fitness (W) of the genotype producing the largest number of offspring by convention is fixed as 1. The other genotype will necessarily produce a number $1 - x$ of offspring, so that $W = 1/(1 - x)$. (See Chapter 3 for more details.) The average fitness of the population $(\overline{W})$ is the summation of the fitness of the individual genotypes. In order to apply this concept a second convention has to be made. At each generation, the population size has to be adjusted so that it appears to be constant (in order to make valid comparisons from generation to generation).

The forces operating within the population will tend to keep $- x$ at a very low value, and $\overline{W}$ at a high one (see Chapter 3). A high value of $\overline{W}$ indicates that there is not much difference in the number of offspring surviving between the genotype producing the highest number of surviving offspring and that with the lowest number of surviving offspring. It also may indicate a rather uniform population. On account of keeping the population size constant in the calculations there is no way of measuring absolute increases in number. Finally, the recombination system will also affect the value of $\overline{W}$; a population with an open system will have a lower value than one with a closed recombination system. Fitness then, although it is the measure of natural selection, fails to give an indication of absolute increases in the number of individuals in a population and a measure of variability. These factors may be important components of what constitutes "evolutionary success."

Another way of measuring success is by measuring the rate of numerical increase in a population, known as r. This is a measure used preferentially by population ecologists. One way of obtaining r is to calculate at any instant in time the birth rate, and subtract from it the death rate. The rate of increase so calculated is dependent on population density, and furthermore all the populations with constant numbers will have a value of $r = 0$. But the average fitness of these populations might be different. In some, little evolution might be taking place, while the possibility exists that in others some genotypes might be actively replacing less fit genotypes in the population.

A different measure of r is obtained when the rate of increase is measured in the early stages of growth of a population (the so-called logarithmic growth phase). Here r (indicated usually as r_0) will give a measure of $\overline{W}$, since the population with the highest average fitness leaves more offspring. But it does not tell us what will happen once the population has attained its normal size.

None of these methods is entirely satisfactory. New ways will have to be discovered. And this aspect is only the beginning of much work in determining what constitutes "evolutionary success." The question is an open one, and one that is being actively investigated. Several models of optimal population structures have been proposed, but none is as yet entirely convincing. Once the solution to this problem is found, it is going to aid materially in predicting what the course of evolution can be under different set conditions.

Present and Past Climate and Its Effect on the Evolution of Organisms

In this chapter we have emphasized the fact that it is the changing environment that is responsible for alterations in selection coefficients that ultimately bring about evolution. A perfectly uniform environment leads to a dynamic equilibrium, and once this is established few changes will take place. Of the factors of the environment, the chief cause of alterations is climate, particularly two components: temperature and moisture. These two variable factors are the ones exerting primary control of the environment. Land-sea relations and mountain systems also change, but not as much. Furthermore rainfall and temperature relationships will affect mountains very much. The earth has gone through warming and cooling trends, wet and dry periods. Each major change has favored whole new lineages of plants and animals that have eventually replaced the former "kings" of creation.

There is another important component of these changes to be examined, the so-called historical factor in evolution. Natural selection does not create anything, but favors the most adapted organism in each habitat. When changes occur in the environment, organisms with structures preadapted to a new situation will be selected. The old habitat determines to a certain extent the composition of the biota of the new one. There is no inherent law saying that man has to walk erect on two legs in order to use his hands; there are many other possibilities, and assorted science fiction Martians are previews of such possibilities. But the historical factors determined what man looks like. Every animal reflects first and foremost the adaptation to the niche it occupies and the specialized role it performs in the habitat, but it is also a reflection of the niches and habitats occupied by its ancestors.

The study of past environments and of the organisms that occupied them belongs to paleontology, the subject of the next chapter.

Suggested Further Reading

Bates, M. "Ecology and Evolution." In S. Tax (ed.), *Evolution After Darwin*, Vol. 1. Chicago: University of Chicago Press, 1960, pp. 547–568.

Dobzhansky, T. "Evolution and Environment." In S. Tax (ed.), *Evolution After Darwin*, Vol. 1. Chicago: University of Chicago Press, 1960, pp. 403–428.

Grant, V. *The Origin of Adaptations.* New York: Columbia University Press, 1963 (especially Chapters 5–6).

Mayr, E. "The Emergence of Evolutionary Novelties." In S. Tax (ed.), *Evolution After Darwin*, Vol. 1. Chicago: University of Chicago Press, 1960, pp. 349–380.

Simpson G. G. *The Major Features of Evolution.* New York: Columbia University Press, 1953 (especially Chapters 6–8).

Stebbins, G. L. *Variation and Evolution in Plants.* New York: Columbia University Press, 1950 (especially Chapters 1–4 and 12–14).

8

Paleontology and Evolution

IN OUR DISCUSSION so far we have analyzed three major components of the theory of evolution. First we discussed genetic variability, which provides the raw materials for evolution. The ultimate causes for the existence of genetic variability are the physical and chemical properties of the substances of which organisms are formed, in particular the nucleic acids, DNA and RNA, and the proteins. These substances assembled into genes and chromosomes provide the continuity of genetic information from generation to generation. At the same time the way chromosomes divide offers the opportunity for errors of duplication to occur, called mutations, and also for rearrangements of the genes to take place so that new syntheses of genetic information are offered. Selection is the second dimension of evolution. Due in part to the overabundance of offspring in terms of the available supply of food, selection will favor the type that is capable of using resources in the most efficient form and as a result leaves the most offspring. The third dimension is provided by a diversified environment which allows for the selection of more than one type over a given area. The final dimension, time, allows an interplay between these aspects. If at any one moment a series of diverse environments are found over the surface of the earth, given enough time a series of diverse environments will succeed each other at any one place. Looking at environmental fluctuations in terms of space and time, a veritable crazy quilt of ever changing conditions can be observed. At each point organisms exist reflecting in their genetic constitution and morphological make-up their adaptation to the then present environmental conditions, as well as the conditions of their immediate ancestors and to a lesser degree of their more remote ancestors. In order to get a true picture of evolution it is essential not to overlook this fourth dimension.

The great diversity of past and present plants and animals is a manifestation of the response of organisms to the fluctuations of the environment over the millennia of time. The origin of living forms from simpler, nonliving substances is in itself a response to changing conditions in the environment. In effect, had the earth not cooled and the elements become distributed over its volume as they were, or had the conditions of temperature and energy been such that water could not have been formed, life would not have originated, at least not in the form familiar to us. The ultimate causes responsible for changes in the environment are extraterrestrial and are not too well understood. Nevertheless, we have a certain comprehension of the types of changes that have occurred on the earth since its inception, particularly those which have taken place in more recent periods. This evidence is provided by the remains of plants and animals that once occupied the surface of the earth and the waters of the sea. These remains are known as fossils (Figure 8·1).

The branch of biology involving the study of fossils and the past conditions of the earth is paleontology. If the shapes and forms of the organisms that inhabited a certain part of the globe in a certain period are known, inferences can be made about the climate of that period by analogy with what we know about the requirements of present-day forms. For example, we know that monkeys are restricted to tropical regions and that they will die if exposed to cold winters. Fossil remains of monkeys have been found in beds corresponding to the geological era called the Tertiary of Patagonia in southern Argentina, a region that today has very cold winters and is unsuited for monkeys. Two explanations are possible: the monkeys of the Tertiary were cold-adapted, or Patagonia in the Tertiary was much warmer than today. The presence of other fossil remains of tropical animals such as anteaters and of tropical trees indicates that in all likelihood the second interpretation is the correct one. In the same fossil beds, remains of other animals are found that today are extinct, such as marsupial saber-tooth tigers and giant sloths. By analogy and extrapolation we can conclude that these animals too preferred warmer climates. Likewise the type of plants with which they were associated can tell us something about their feeding habits and the type of environment they lived in.

The paleontologist then tries to reconstruct the life and the environments of the past, based on the assumption that the response of living things to the environment was the same then as it is today. This inference is in part conjectural, but has its basis of fact in the study of chemical substances extracted from fossil beds. Analysis of fossils, as well as of meteorites and of the light that comes to us from stars millions of light-years away, which emanated in many cases before the earth was formed, shows that the chemical com-

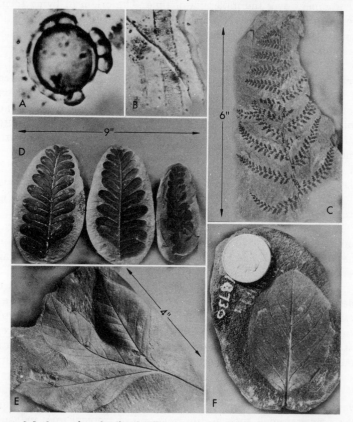

Figure 8·1. **Some plant fossils of different ages.** A: *Eosphaera tileri* (Precambrian); B: *Ammikea septata* (Precambrian). A and B are among the oldest remains of living organisms known. C: *Sphenopteris* sp. (Mazon Creek, Ill., upper Carboniferous); D: *Alethopteris* sp. (Mazon Creek, Ill., upper Carboniferous); E: *Sassafras* sp. (Dakota sandstone, middle Cretaceous); F: *Diospyros rotundifolia* (Dakota sandstone, middle Cretaceous). Note how the plants become more familiar as we move forward through time. [Photos courtesy Professor E. S. Barghorn.]

position of these bodies is the same as that found today and that these chemical substances display a similar behavior. These results back the conclusion that the building blocks of the universe are the same and that there is only one kind of matter. It follows that natural laws have always operated in the same way as they do today, and if this is so, the behavior of living things in the past must have been similar to that of present-day organisms. We know of species having evolved with little or no superficial morphological modification but considerable internal and presumably physiological modification. It is highly unlikely that most species have evolved in such manner.

How Fossils Are Formed

The word "fossil" is derived from the Latin word for digging up. We may define a fossil as any recognizable organic structure, or impression of such a structure, preserved from prehistoric times. This includes bones, wood, skin, pollen, and also tracks, dung, burrows, or any other remains formed by a prehistoric organism, or one which gives an indication of the presence of such an organism.

The body of most dead plants and animals decomposes sooner or later. If this were not so, the surface of the earth would be covered several miles thick by the remains of dead animals, and actually life would probably have ceased long ago. All available mineral matter would have become encased in the bodies of organisms. Decomposition is caused by several agents. Scavengers of all sorts from vultures to bacteria and fungi take care of the soft parts very rapidly. Harder tissues such as bones and wood are more resistant. Nevertheless, enzymes secreted by certain fungi and bacteria, acids occurring naturally in the soil, and the combined action of environmental agents such as water, wind, and temperature destroy even the hardest organic remains with time. However, under very special circumstances some parts may be preserved with varying amounts of modification, to form fossils (Figure 8·2).

For preservation to take place, rapid burial after death in a substance that protects the organism from destruction by scavengers and weathering is needed. The most common substance is some heavy silt or mud, and burial will occur more frequently in water than on land, and in colder areas than in warm ones. But other substances can serve as well. Some of the best fossils are found in amber, which is a fossil resin. Particularly small insects, which probably got stuck in the resin and could not free themselves, are found in amber. Some very well preserved remains of woolly mammoths and rhinoceroses from the Pleistocene age have been found frozen in Siberia. Volcanic ash also can create good conditions for preservation. But even when rapidly buried the soft parts of an organism decompose, and in most cases only the hard parts remain. Shells which are inorganic in nature are usually preserved com-

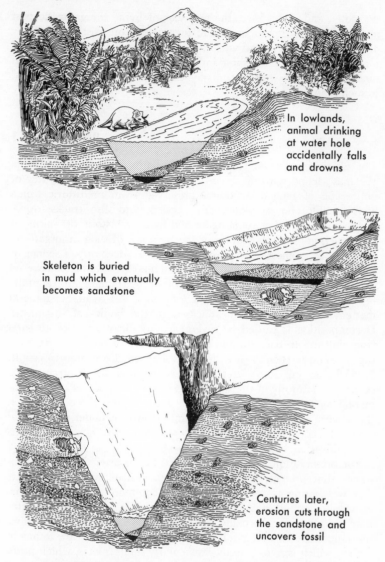

In lowlands, animal drinking at water hole accidentally falls and drowns

Skeleton is buried in mud which eventually becomes sandstone

Centuries later, erosion cuts through the sandstone and uncovers fossil

Figure 8·2. Schematic representation of the process of fossilization.

pletely unaltered; bones and wood, on the other hand, are often mineralized (commonly referred to as petrified)—that is, the free spaces in the tissue are impregnated with mineral substances carried by ground water. In other cases the totality of the plant or animal structure is destroyed, leaving an empty space that nevertheless faithfully reflects the exterior aspects of the dead organism; such a fossil is a mold. If the space is subsequently filled by a foreign substance, this is a cast (Figure 8·3).

After burial the fossil may be very much altered. The commonest type of alteration is flattening due to pressure as more and more layers of sediment are piled on top of the bed containing the fossil.

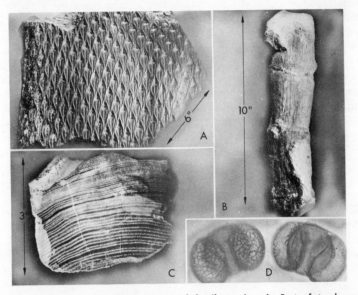

Figure 8·3. Examples of different types of fossil remains. A: Part of trunk and bark of *Lepidodendron* sp. (Carboniferous). This is an impression made by the original plant on the rock. B: Stem fragment of *Calamites* sp. (Carboniferous). This is an original pith cast. C: Section of silicified wood of *Gleditchia montanense* (Miocene). D: Fossil pollen grains of pine (*Pinus* sp.) from the Eocene of Oregon. [A—C: Photos courtesy Professor E. S. Barghorn; D: courtesy Dr. A. Graham.]

The bed may be further altered by folding and lateral movements. Eventually it has to be uncovered by erosion if we are to get possession of the fossil, and it might be further damaged in this process. Some fossils have been exposed in the past and reburied. Consequently, the chances of recovering an intact specimen are very slender, particularly with specimens of great age.

The Problem of the Missing Parts

The paleontologist is presented in most, if not all, cases with a fossil that represents a highly modified remnant, usually incomplete, of life from the past. He wants to learn as much as possible about it and the conditions in which the organism lived. The first thing to do is to classify the fossil and relate it if possible to some known group. This is no minor problem with an incomplete and modified fragmentary fossil remain of an extinct organism. In many cases the fossil will have key structures such as teeth, jaws, or skulls preserved, but in many other instances only a femur or a rib or a tarsus has been found. Since these structures can give at best only an approximate idea of the animal, paleontologists use the device of form species. Each remain is given a specific name and recorded as a different species, and an educated guess is made as to its possible affinities. If later on, a more complete skeleton is found and two or more form species are shown to be but parts of the same organism, the form species names are abandoned in favor of the correct name of the animal, which now can be classified more precisely. Form species permit the paleontologist to deal in a scientific way with incomplete remains that otherwise would be useless. Particularly the paleobotanist is aided by this device (Figure 8·3). In effect vertebrate animals by and large can be identified by the remains of their bones and teeth, which are the structures most likely to be preserved. Not so with plants. Wood and leaf impressions that are the most common plant fossils are often insufficient material to identify with any certainty the group to which they belonged.

Dating Fossils: Relative and Absolute Ages

If fossil specimens are to be of any value, their age must be known. To determine the age of fossiliferous beds paleontologists use fossils! This may seem like a paradox, but actually is not. William Smith, the father of modern geology, as early as 1790 made the observation that different geological strata were characterized by unique assemblages of fossils, and that consequently particular strata could be identified by their fossil contents, even when their physical characteristics were changed. In areas where little or no disturbance had occurred the order of deposition of the strata could be ascertained, since obviously the overlying beds must have been deposited after the ones below them. By then comparing the fossils of beds from different areas a relative chronology could be established, known as the geological column (Table 8·1). A harder task was to establish time intervals in years, and until recently there was no accurate way of doing it. In the last fifteen years, methods of obtaining more exact ages based on radioactive decomposition of

TABLE 8·1
The Geological Column

TIME SINCE RECENT IN MILLIONS OF YEARS	APPROXIMATE DURATION IN MILLIONS OF YEARS	ERA	PERIOD	EPOCH	SOME IMPORTANT EVOLUTIONARY EVENTS
1	1	Cenozoic	Quaternary	Recent, Pleistocene	Advent of man
63	62	Cenozoic	Tertiary	Pliocene, Miocene, Oligocene, Eocene, Paleocene	Development of modern families of mammals, birds and flowering plants
135	72	Mesozoic	Cretaceous		First flowering plants
181	46	Mesozoic	Jurassic		Age of Reptiles; gymnosperms
230	59	Mesozoic	Triassic		
280	50	Paleozoic	Permian		Radiation of Amphibians; first reptiles
345	65	Paleozoic	Carboniferous		
405	60	Paleozoic	Devonian		First land plants and first land animals
425	20	Paleozoic	Silurian		
500	75	Paleozoic	Ordovician		Jawless vertebrates; first sharks
600	100	Paleozoic	Cambrian		
approx. 3,500?	approx. 3,000	Precambrian			First forms of life, approx. 2,500,000,000

elements in rocks have been devised. These methods have shown that the age of the earth estimated by the old methods was less than the actual age. The application of these methods also confirmed the correctness of the relative ages used by the paleontologist.

To date a fossil bed, the paleontologist looks for fossils known to be restricted to a certain geological stratum, with which he establishes the relative age of the bed. All the unknown fossils in the bed are then given the same age. It is of paramount importance to make sure of the location of the fossils in the bed and to know the overlying and underlying beds, since fossils are known to have been moved in and out of strata in the course of geological time. At present, when possible, samples are also collected with which ages are obtained by radioactive measurement methods.

The Concept of Species in Time and Space

We have defined species as a group of potentially interbreeding populations. We also indicated that species is the only natural non-arbitrary category as opposed to the higher categories, which are arbitrary. But if we take into account the fourth dimension of evolution, our concept of interbreeding is no longer applicable. A present-day horse is not capable of interbreeding with one that lived in the middle ages, not even with one having lived in the last century, and much less so with horses of the Pleistocene. Do all these horses then constitute distinct species? Evidently not. But species in time lack the limits assigned to contemporary species on the basis of their breeding behavior. Furthermore, with the passage of time, the populations evolve and pass imperceptibly from one into another.

The problem is still further compounded by the scantiness of the fossil record, so that in very few instances does the paleontologist have a good sample of the variability of the species at a given time level. Breaks in the continuity of the fossil record are usually (all too often) the species limits. The early form has by then evolved enough so that on morphological grounds (and again here analogy with corresponding modern species is applied, so that fossil species are separated when the morphological differences are comparable to modern species) it can be considered a different species. But there is always the possibility that if the intermediate forms were known, they would form a continuous series. A good example of this is the confused terminology of human ancestors, where practically every skull has at one time been given a different generic name! The paleontologist, of course, does not know, unless he has a continuous series through time, whether the earlier form is indeed an ancestor of the more modern one, and the evolution of the horse is a case in point.

THE EVOLUTION OF THE HORSE FAMILY (EQUIDAE).

The Equidae are represented today by one genus with six species: *Equus caballus* (the horse), *E. asinus* (African donkey), *E. hemionus* (Asiatic donkey), and three species of zebras: *E. zebra, E. grevyi,* and *E. quagga*. The genus *Equus* originated in the late Pliocene, but the horse family goes back 60 million years to the Eocene period. The Equidae developed out of the ancestral stock of a primitive and long-extinct order of mammals called condylarths that lived at the beginning of the Tertiary period. The first known member of the horse family to arise from the condylarths is *Hyracotherium*. It was somewhat doglike in size and shape, with a small head and a large tail, and stood 25 cm. high in some species and up to 50 cm. in others. It had padded feet (like present-day dogs) with four toes on the forefeet and three on the hind feet, and the toes ended in small separate hoofs. As indicated by the low-crowned, simple-cusped teeth with low ridges, *Hyracotherium* fed on succulent leaves, small fruits, and soft seeds. Consequently it must have been a browsing, forest-inhabiting animal. Although it lived in the New and Old World, the horse family evolved mostly in North America with repeated invasions into the Old World (Figure 8·4).

By the Oligocene epoch *Hyracotherium* had evolved into the genus *Mesohippus*. This was somewhat larger, with padded feet, but only three toes on all four legs, and a more horselike head with set-back eyes and an elongated muzzle. The brain had also increased in size, and the teeth although basically like *Hyracotherium* had larger crests. In the Miocene epoch we find *Merychippus,* a considerably larger animal, which stood about 1 meter tall. The more advanced species of this genus have lost the foot pads, and although they still stand on three toes, the body is carried largely on the hoof of the central toe. The teeth now possess high crowns, a complex pattern of crests, and cement which its ancestors' teeth lacked. This is indicative that the animal no longer lived in the forest but in savannalike habitats and that its diet was mainly one of grass. *Pliohippus* was a one-toed grazing horse which roamed the North American plains in the Pliocene era and from which *Equus* arose at the end of this period. Compared to its ancestors, *Equus* is large, with single-toed feet and large hoofs and with high-crowned and elaborately crested and ridged teeth, adapted to a diet of the

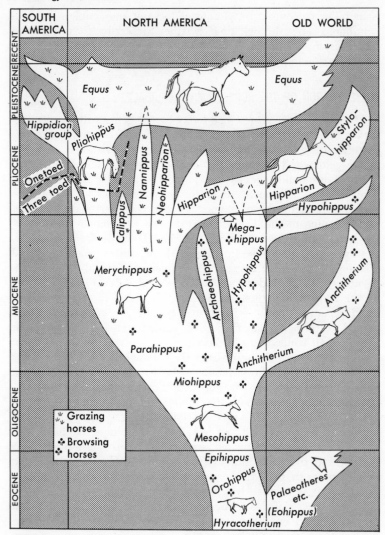

Figure 8·4. The lineages of the horse family. The restorations are to scale. [Redrawn from G. G. Simpson, *Horses* (1950), by courtesy of Oxford University Press.]

grass he lives on. It has become extinct in the New World but survives in the Old World.

In addition to this main line of descent, different other sidelines developed, such as *Anchiterium, Archaeohippus,* and *Hypohippus* in the Eocene, and *Hipparion, Nannipus,* and *Neohipparion* in the Pliocene (Figure 8·4). The horse family is probably the one group whose fossil record is best known. In regions where they are represented by a good fossil record, the transition from one genus to the next successive one is a gradual one, and consequently the dividing lines between the genera are arbitrary.

The fossil record of the Equidae exemplifies the appearance and ultimate fixation of adaptive characteristics. It is particularly well illustrated in the evolution of the teeth. One of the cheek teeth of *Equus* has a short projection called a crochet. This projection is absent in most specimens of *Mesohippus* and other Oligocene horses. But occasional individuals, which undoubtedly represent a mutant type, have a small crochet. In *Miohippus* the crochet is present in more individuals, but there are still some which lack it. In the Miocene-aged *Parahippus,* the crochet has become universal in all populations, but it is still small. It became larger later in the ancestors of *Equus*. A similar situation holds for the appearance of cement in *Parahippus* and its successor *Merychippus* in the Miocene. The appearance of cement is first sporadic but eventually becomes general and later increased in thickness. This corresponds to the time when the horses moved from browsing to grazing. The harder grass required harder wearing teeth. Cement, which is a reinforcing material for grinding teeth, was obviously of selective advantage. So also were the development of more elaborate crests on the grinding surface of the cheek teeth and the increase in size of the crown. It is interesting to note that the development of all these characteristics proceeded with greater speed in the Miocene with the appearance of grazing horses.

Rates of Evolution

The evolution of the horse family also illustrates very nicely the fact that evolution does not proceed at a steady rate, nor always in the same direction. This should by now be obvious from all that has been said about the way natural selection operates. We have seen how in the Equidae the change in environment from forest-living browsers to plains-living grazers brought about an increase in the rate of evolution of those structures that were most affected by the new situations, in particular the teeth. There were also an increase in size and a change from padded feet to the springlike action of present-day *Equus*. In other lineages there have been few or no changes during the time the horses were evolving. This is illustrated by the opossum, which has changed very little since the late Cretaceous, some 80 million years ago.

There is no reason either for evolution to proceed always in the same direction. Although *Equus* is considerably larger than *Hyracotherium,* it is smaller than some ancestral Pliocene species of *Equus.* In addition some extinct Pliocene horses not ancestral to *Equus* like *Megahippus* and *Hypohippus* are still larger, while others such as *Calippus* and *Nannipus* are considerably smaller.

The differences in evolutionary rates can be attributed primarily to the changes or lack of them in the environment. After a lineage has reached a high adaptive level, few changes will take place in a uniform environment. A rapidly changing environment, on the other hand, will constantly produce new selective requirements to which organisms will have to adapt. In addition to the environment, intrinsic factors also play a role. All those characteristics that increase variability (such as large populations, high number of chromosomes, short generations, and so on) are advantageous in times of environmental fluctuations, and organisms possessing them will evolve at a faster rate.

A final point to be drawn from our brief analysis of the fossil record, which is also well illustrated by the Equidae, is that the fate of most, if not all, species and genera is extinction. Some—the minority—become transformed into more evolved types, but the majority eventually can no longer adapt to the ever present new environmental conditions or compete with better adapted organisms, and they become extinct. This has been the fate of 17 out of 18 genera of Equidae (Figure 8·4) and of nine-tenths of all species!

In conclusion, the fossil record provides considerable evidence for the soundness of the synthetic theory of evolution. Nevertheless fossils, contrary to widely held views, due largely to the incompleteness of the fossil record and its nonrandomness, do not by themselves provide the proof of evolution. Only the combined and judicious application of data taken from fossils, living organisms, and experiments can provide an approximate justification for Darwin's theory.

Suggested Further Reading

Kummel, B. *History of the Earth*. San Francisco: Freeman & Co., 1961.
Simpson, G. G. *The Meaning of Evolution*. New Haven, Conn.: Yale University Press, 1949.
———. *Horses*. New York: Oxford University Press, 1951.

Taxonomy and Evolution

UNDERSTANDING THE WORLD of organisms that surround us requires the ordering of the multitude of forms into some sort of rational system. Consequently systematics is as old as man's quest for knowledge, and the effort to classify and understand the variability of animals and plants has led to the development of all the other branches of biology. The information obtained by these more specialized approaches has in turn affected and profoundly modified the field of taxonomy, transforming it from a mere effort to classify into the scientific enterprise of discovering and understanding the reasons for the apparent order of nature.

Modern Taxonomy

Although the rate of change has been steadily increasing, the transformation of taxonomy into a science has been a slow one. Obviously, not until a provisional circumscription of each of the classes of organisms has been undertaken, and they in turn classed into larger groups, such as genera, families, orders, and classes, can any serious effort to study the reasons for their existence be made. So far, about 1,500,000 species have been described and classified. Of the major groups of animals and plants, only the birds with about 8,650 species and perhaps also the gymnosperms among plants with about 650 species have been more or less completely surveyed. Our knowledge of the kinds and numbers of all the other groups is incomplete, and although forecasts of the number of undescribed species are highly conjectural, it has been estimated that there are more than 100,000 undescribed species of flowering plants, 20,000 species of fishes, and over 1,000,000 of insects! The end to the work of describing and classifying the kinds of organisms is clearly not in sight.

But the work of the systematist does not stop with description and classification of species. He wants to know the genetic relationships and the history of the species he works with and the mechanisms that brought them into being. He also wants to discover laws governing the behavior of all organisms. As biologists working in other disciplines learn more about the chemistry, physiology, anatomy, and behavior of plants and animals, taxonomists are deluged with a wealth of information to consider in attempting to formulate classificatory and evolutionary interpretations. Probably nobody is more aware of the scientific information explosion than the small band of working taxonomists! At the same time, increased understanding of all aspects of organismic function and behavior has made systematics more interesting and exciting than ever, and this oldest of biological disciplines is experiencing a burst of activity as never before.

In this book we have analyzed the impact on taxonomy of some of the newer branches of biology such as cytology, genetics, and the behavioral sciences, as well as more classical fields such as ecology and paleontology. It must be remembered that the impulse for the development of these sciences was given by taxonomy, and that the spillover from the other disciplines that systematics is experiencing is a feedback from the early spillover of systematics. It might therefore be useful to survey briefly some historical developments and the methods and procedures of taxonomy.

The Principles of Classification

Classification is the ordering of organisms (or any other objects) into classes. The organisms in each class are held together by some system of relationship among them. Language is a primitive form of classification in which each class of "things" is given a designation (noun). All the members of a class are held together by the possession of common characters or relationships. The first step in classification is the delimitation of the classes; the second step is the establishment of relationships between the classes and the formation of a hierarchy. Relationships can be established in two ways: first, by overlapping or coincidence of nonidentical classes, and second, by subordination of some classes to others or the inclusion of one class within another. As an example of overlapping, there can be a class of long-furred dogs and a class of brown-furred dogs, which are nonidentical. A class of long-furred, brown-colored dogs overlaps both of the given classes and is coextensive with the overlap of the two.

Classification by subordination and inclusion of classes is used in language together with overlapping. "Red foxes," "gray foxes," "arctic foxes," all belong to the larger and inclusive class "fox." Its use in biological classification goes back to Aristotelian logic. In biological classification, ordering by subordination and inclusion of classes is the usual method. All classes are included in larger ones. For example, the species *Felis felis* (the cat), *Felis concolor* (the puma), *Felis tigris* (the tiger), and *Felis onca* (the jaguar), are all included in the genus *Felis*. In turn the genus *Felis* is included in the family Felidae, in the order Carnivora, and in the class Mammalia. Such an arrangement is a hierarchy.

According to this method, a species consists of its "genus" plus its "differentia." The "genus" is all the properties common to all the species of the next inclusive class (called also in this case the genus) and by which it is defined. The "differentia" are the characteristics by which we differentiate one species from another within a given genus. The family is likewise defined by the characteristics common to all the genera included in the family ("the genus" of the family), and so on with each higher class. This method of classification is useful if we are interested in establishing an order based only on the logical relationships between the genus and its species, and among the species themselves. So if we define the genus *Felis* by the possession of tails, if we rigidly apply Aristotelian logic we would have to exclude bobtailed cats from the genus (and also from the species *Felis felis,* the cat). But obviously, bobtailed cats belong both to the species *Felis felis* and to the genus *Felis*.

In practice we classify on the basis of the totality of the characters of the organism and not primarily on the basis of logical consistency. If an animal lacks some of the "genus" characters but has all the others, we maintain it in the class to which it would belong if it had the missing characteristics. The scientific justification for this procedure is given by evolutionary theory. In adapting to different environments populations may change in any way, and both the "genus" and the "differentia" are likely to change. Species are defined, whenever possible, primarily in terms of genetic and breeding relationships, and only secondarily in terms of morphological characteristics. This presents a problem. If related classes (in a phylogenetic sense) do not have any common characteristics, how can a higher, inclusive class be defined? A partial answer to this problem is given by set theory. A genus in set theory is defined in terms of several characteristics (the more the better), and each species must have at least a minimum number of these characteristics in order to be included in the genus. This procedure would be completely satisfactory if the phylogenetic relationships were known. But this is seldom the case. As a matter of fact, once the classification is established, a phylogeny is deduced from it.

In taxonomic practice, an empirical, pragmatic approach is used, which combines elements of Aristotelian logic, set theory, and evolutionary theory. Field observation and experimentation, supplemented by museum and herbarium studies, provide information on variability and breeding relationships of populations. On the basis of these data the elementary classes, the species, are established. Using the totality of the known characteristics of all the species, genera are then established, so that the degree of difference separating the members of the same genus is less than that separating the species of different genera. This can be done in two ways. One is by a strictly statistical approach, where as many characters as possible are quantified and multiple correlations established by the use of high-speed digital computers. This method is logically consistent in terms of set theory. Its greatest drawback is that all aspects of the phenotype are given the same importance. But we know that some are determined by a few genes, and others by large series of genes; and furthermore certain characteristics of the organism (those of immediate adaptive value) are very plastic, while others (such as reproductive structures) are not. In other words, the phylogenetic significance of these characters is different because the rate at which they can evolve is very different. The usual procedure is therefore to weigh characters according to their potential phylogenetic significance and to establish higher classes accordingly. The great drawback of this procedure is that it introduces a subjective element (weighting of characters), but it has been upheld so far in those cases where a phylogenetic check (via the fossil record) has been provided.

Taxonomy, Systematics, Classification, and Nomenclature

These four terms are often used interchangeably, leading to much confusion. We have said already that classification is the ordering of organisms into classes. Systematics is the comparative study of any group of organisms and of any and all relationships among them using the techniques of one or more branches of biology. Systematic studies often (but not always) result in classifications. Likewise, classifications may or may not be based on systematic studies, but present-day biological classifications are almost exclusively so based. This tends to equate these two operations as

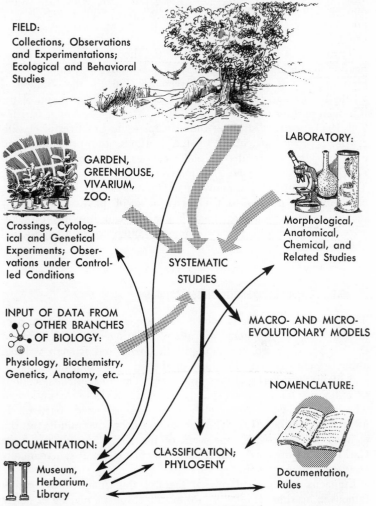

FIELD:

Collections, Observations and Experimentations; Ecological and Behavioral Studies

GARDEN, GREENHOUSE, VIVARIUM, ZOO:

Crossings, Cytological and Genetical Experiments; Observations under Controlled Conditions

LABORATORY:

Morphological, Anatomical, Chemical, and Related Studies

SYSTEMATIC STUDIES

INPUT OF DATA FROM OTHER BRANCHES OF BIOLOGY:

Physiology, Biochemistry, Genetics, Anatomy, etc.

MACRO- AND MICRO-EVOLUTIONARY MODELS

NOMENCLATURE:

DOCUMENTATION:

Museum, Herbarium, Library

CLASSIFICATION; PHYLOGENY

Documentation, Rules

Figure 9·1. Some of the operations involved in systematic and evolutionary studies. Arrows indicate direction of informational flow.

synonymous. Nomenclature, on the other hand, is the application of distinctive names to each of the groups recognized in any classification. A set of arbitrary rules, embodied in the "codes" of botanical and zoological nomenclature, govern the application of names to plants and animals. These rules, which have been elaborated over the years, combine historical elements (like the rules of priority in naming species) with practical rulings to insure clarity and ease in use. Nomenclature is a device to eliminate confusion and insure one common language in biological classification (Figure 9·1).

Taxonomy is variously defined as "the theoretical study of classification, including its bases, principles, procedures and rules" (G. G. Simpson, *Principles of Animal Taxonomy*, 1961); "the synthesis of all the facts about [organisms] into a concept and expression of the interrelationships of [organisms]" (H. L. Mason, *Madroño, 10:*193–208, 1950); or the "study of the principles and practices of classification, . . . in particular . . . the methods, the principles, and even in part the results of biological classification" (J. Heslop-Harrison, *New Concepts in Flowering Plant Taxonomy*, 1953). The relationship of taxonomy to systematics is somewhat like that of theoretical physics to the whole field of physics. Taxonomy includes classification and nomenclature, but leans heavily on systematics for its concepts. The two areas are often erroneously equated as being the same.

Artificial, Natural, and Phylogenetic Classifications

The earliest classifications known to us are eminently practical ones aiming solely at a system that allows ordering of the elements of the environment. So, for example, in Greek and Roman writing, animals were divided into those of the sea, the land, and the air, and plants into herbs, shrubs, and trees. These early classifications of antiquity, known to us mainly from the works of Aristotle and Theophrastus, were slowly elaborated and perfected, particularly after the Middle Ages. They culminated by the middle of the eighteenth century with the work of the great Swedish naturalist Carl Linne (Linnaeus), which marks the first effort at systematically classifying all organisms.

Linnaeus' system had several features that made it deservedly famous in his time. It allowed, for example, for the placing of newly discovered entities without disruption of the system; the basic taxa, genera and species, were by and large fairly well delimited; and a very practical method of binary nomenclature was presented, which has persisted until this day. Nevertheless, Linnaeus' concept of the species was essentially the same as Aristotle's, based exclusively on morphological similarities, and his higher categories, although logically consistent, were often based on trivial characteristics. Linnaeus was a keen observer and had a questioning mind, which led him among other things to conduct experiments on hybridization and inheritance in plants. This notwithstanding, Linnaeus believed, as did most naturalists of his time, in the immutability of species, which supposedly had been created once by a superior being in the same way and in the same number as they were known then. Consequently Linnaeus, who was a very pious man, did not attempt to discover a grand scheme of order in the universe. His practical and religious outlook probably did not permit him to do so.

It was the next generation of naturalists, in particular the French biologists, who attempted to find this grand scheme. The root of this movement goes back to the beginning of the scientific revolution. The discovery by Newton and Leibnitz of the laws of gravity and the movement of celestial bodies, and the impact of the ideas and methods of Bacon and Descartes, produced a search for the discovery of the laws of nature. This search eventually produced a new outlook about the biological world. Species were still believed by most to have been created by a superior being, but the creator was supposed to have had a grand scheme in mind, and the purpose of the systematists was to discover it. A search for the so-called natural affinities of organisms was initiated. This led to a great deal of good work in the course of which true evolutionary relationships were discovered, although at the time they were not recognized as such. This ferment also gave considerable impetus to the study of comparative anatomy and saw the beginnings of serious studies in physiology.

Among the earliest of the French naturalists espousing this new view was Buffon and his protégé Lamarck, who worked in the second half of the eighteenth century. Lamarck was the author of one of the first systems in which species were not considered immutable but the result of some kind of evolution. The movement flourished in France and to a somewhat lesser extent in Germany and England. Aside from Buffon and Lamarck, the names of Geoffrey, De Candolle, the German Oken, and the Englishman Erasmus Darwin should be mentioned.

The "natural systems" were not a total break with the artificial system of Linnaeus. Aristotelian logic still was, at least in theory, the rationale of the classifications. But a greater effort was made to study the totality of the characters of an organism and to try to have the classifications reflect natural affinities. This led to a more empirical approach to classification in which logical concepts that we would associate today with set theory were applied.

The naturalists of the first half of the nineteenth century were very near to the discovery of the theory of evolution. In their writings we can read many modern-sounding discourses about the relationships between plants and animals. They probably did not arrive at the point of proposing an evolving biota for lack of a mechanism to explain the change. Darwin's greatest contribution was therefore not so much the idea of evolution as his theory of natural selection, which provided a mechanism for evolution. Lamarck, and others after his time, had proposed systems in which species became transformed, but they were not accepted because these authors could not present a rational explanation as to how this might have come about.

The formulation and acceptance of the theory of natural selection did not immediately affect contemporary classifications. This was largely because of the excellent work of the systematists of the time, who in their search for "natural affinities" had discovered evolutionary affinities. Darwin himself acknowledged the influence his four-volume work on the classification of barnacles had on his formulation of the theory of evolution. Taxonomists after Darwin changed the phrase "natural" affinities to "phylogenetic" affinities, but for some time did not drastically modify their mode of work.

The rediscovery in 1900 of Mendel's laws of inheritance at first brought a reaction against Darwin. Particulate inheritance was interpreted initially as denying natural selection. How could the accumulation of small changes account for evolution, if characters were inherited as discrete units? This reaction against Darwinism was due in part to the drastic effects which some of the first-discovered mutations had. It was also due in part to the unfortunate choice of the plant genus *Oenothera,* the evening primrose, as research material by Hugo de Vries (one of the rediscoverers of Mendel's laws and the strongest opponent of natural selection). In species of this genus, morphological changes occur that were misinterpreted at the time as inheritable mutations. Nevertheless it was not long before Mendelism and Darwinism were united. More and better insight into genetic phenomena and the development of population genetics were most prominent in effecting this marriage. It eventually led to the formulation of the synthetic theory of evolution.

The prominent feature of the synthetic theory is a change from a typological mode of thinking to one that emphasizes populations. A feature of the Linnaean system that was still adhered to at the turn of the century was the Platonic concept of the *eidos* (idea, type, essence). This principle was embodied in the concept of the type—that is, the idealization of an individual as a representative of all the other individuals of the species. The idea of the type was a direct outgrowth of the period when it was believed that each species was immutable. In this case a single specimen—the type—would be a sufficient sample of the species. Darwin recognized the importance of variability, but typological thinking did not cease at that time, partially because the dynamics of population evolution were not known. Only with the development of genetics and the realization that the population and not the individual is the unit of evolution did the thinking of systematists shift from considering individual specimens to studying series and mass samples and to moving whenever possible out of the museum into the field. The concept of "type" as the embodiment of the *eidos* of the species was abandoned, although types are still used as nomenclatural devices.

The second big impact of the synthetic theory on systematics was the change in the concept of the species. Linnaeus defined species according to the dicta of Aristotelian logic. In his definition "the differentia" were stressed, since "the genus" was common to a whole group of species. His concept emphasized differences rather than similarities and consequently obscured relationships. The lack of knowledge in Linnaeus' time about genetics and reproduction precluded the use of any other characters than strictly morphological ones. The lack of good optical equipment further restricted the use of morphological characters to the more gross and superficial ones. Biologists of the nineteenth century, on the other hand, stressed the totality of characters of an organism in their search for natural affinities, and the similarities as well as the differences between organisms were considered in their classification. The development of physiology, anatomy, embryology, and (toward the end of the century) cytology and genetics vastly increased the available criteria. Systematic studies became the basis of biological classifications in most instances, a situation that still holds. Darwinian theory provided for the first time a solid theoretical framework. This led scientists to emphasize similarities as well as differences between species. Nevertheless the concept of the species did not change too drastically from that of Linnaeus.

It was the tremendous growth of genetics in the first half of the twentieth century and the development of the synthetic theory that brought about a major change in the concept of the species. Reproductive relationships became the principal criterion in defining species. This new species definition is closely tied to the emphasis given in the synthetic theory to breeding populations.

The Task Ahead

At the beginning of this chapter we pointed out the immensity of the task of naming and describing organisms that lies ahead. But taxonomy has now become a more rigorous scientific discipline than it was in the time of Linnaeus, with a set of basic tenets and a theoretical framework. Present-day taxonomists can often make predictions and design experiments to check these predictions. Resulting classifications are consequently much richer in informational content. A species name in Linnaeus' time was a means to designate a plant or an animal species, but not much more than that. A name in a modern classification is the key to all that is known about it, its past history, and its relationship with other organisms, since we know so much more about the organisms it designates.

Nevertheless taxonomy has its limitations too. The major stumbling block is the lack of evidence concerning extinct organisms and ignorance about the direction of evolutionary trends and rates of evolution. This creates a major problem, since unless this information is available, weighting of characters in classification is always going to be largely subjective, and a truly phylogenetic classification will never be obtained.

Skeptics may therefore question the validity of an attempt to classify organisms so that the classification will reflect their past history, when that history is unknown. The careful study of the genetics, cytology, structure, function, behavior, and ecological relationships can give us many clues to the past, as we have seen in this book. The judicious application of these data can produce a classification that approximates the past better than the artificial classifications of two centuries ago. It should be remembered that science can at best present a statistical approximation to reality, and the best we can hope for is relative truth.

Suggested Further Reading

Davis, P. H., and V. H. Heywood. *Principles of Angiosperm Taxonomy.* Edinburgh: Oliver & Boyd, 1963 (especially Chapters 1–4).

Heslop-Harrison, J. *New Concepts in Flowering-Plant Taxonomy.* London: W. Heineman, 1953.

Mason, H. L. "Taxonomy, Systematic Botany and Biosystematics." *Madroño, 10*:193–208, 1950.

Simpson, G. G. *Principles of Animal Taxonomy.* New York: Columbia University Press, 1961 (especially Chapters 1–2).

Index